An Early Neolithic Village in the Jordan Valley
PART II:
The Fauna of Netiv Hagdud

T0311539

American School of Prehistoric Research
Bulletin 44

Peabody Museum of Archaeology and Ethnology
Harvard University

An Early Neolithic Village in the Jordan Valley
PART II:
The Fauna of Netiv Hagdud

■

Eitan Tchernov
The Hebrew University of Jerusalem

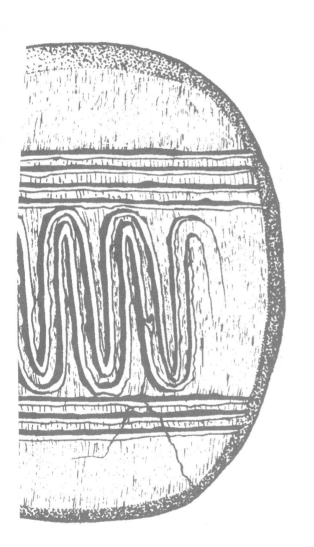

Peabody Museum of Archaeology and Ethnology
Harvard University
Cambridge, MA 1994

Cover Illustration: Engraved pebble found at the
site of Netiv Hagdud.
Drawing: Dahlia Enoch-Shilo.

Design: Janis Owens
Layout: Amy Hirschfeld
Manufactured in the United States of America

Copyright © 1994 by The President and
Fellows of Harvard College

ISBN: 0-87365-548-6
Library of Congress
Catalog Card Number: 94-066686

Preface

THE EARLY NEOLITHIC MOUND OF NETIV HAGDUD IS LOCATed next to a modern village bearing the same name. The site was discovered in the early 1970s while a water reservoir for the village was being built. Following a brief visit to the site it became clear to us that, in order to avoid further damage to the mound, systematic excavations would have to be carried out. Taking immediate action was important in view of the small number of known Pre-Pottery Neolithic A (PPNA) sites in the Levant. A short field season of test excavation (Bar-Yosef et al. 1980) was followed by a systematic survey of the nearby region, known as the es-Salibiya basin (Schuldenrein and Goldberg 1982). Several Natufian sites and one Khiamian site (Salibiya IX) were discovered during the survey. Subsequent quarrying activities led to the initiation of additional test trenches including at Salibiya IX (Bar-Yosef 1980a). During three seasons of excavation undertaken in 1983, 1984, and 1986, 500 square meters of the site of Netiv Hagdud were exposed. The results of the excavations of Netiv Hagdud as well as those of Salibiya IX are presented in Part I.

Before the commencement of excavations at Netiv Hagdud, we formulated a series of questions, as we believed that these salvage excavations could address more general queries and eventually lead to more than just the accumulation of additional data. Aware of how little was known about intrasite organization, size of households, and activities within early village communities, we felt that the chance discovery and excavations of the Netiv Hagdud mound offered an opportunity to increase our body of knowledge concerning PPNA settlements. The excavations were thus designed to address both the question of intrasite structure and organization and aspects of diet and economy based on careful recovery of faunal and floral remains.

From the onset of the field research we made an effort to place the project within the framework of archaeological research into the origins of agriculture in southwest Asia. Since the 1950s, field work in the Near East has advanced considerably due in part to the contributions of numerous European and American scholars inspired by the work of Robert Braidwood and his associates on the hilly flanks of the Zagros and Taurus mountains. In spite of the geopolitical limitations of the last four decades, archaeological data from Early Neolithic period sites were systematically collected, even if not always promptly published. The major research challenges centered on the issues of sedentism, early cultivation, and plant domestication, and the emergence of animal husbandry. The sequence that began with hunter-gatherers of the late Paleolithic or Epipaleolithic and ended with the establishment of Neolithic farming communities left archaeological remains all over the region. From time to time scholars ventured to provide syntheses of the accumulated evidence with or without explicit explanatory models. Summaries of the available information often treated the entire Near East as a geographic unit (e.g., Braidwood and Braidwood 1953; Braidwood and Howe 1960; Braidwood 1975; Braidwood and Braidwood 1986; Mellaart 1975; Hassan 1977; Cauvin 1978, 1981, 1987, 1994; Redman 1978; Moore 1983, 1985; Zeist 1986; Henry 1989b; Bar-Yosef and Belfer-Cohen 1989, 1991, 1992). In addition, other scholars treated the general region of the Near East either as a whole or simply as one of the areas where agriculture was established as a subsistence system (e.g., Bender 1981; Cohen 1977; Hassan 1977, 1981; Redding 1988; Hayden 1990).

The fragmentary archaeological record of the Late Pleistocene limits our understanding of the socioeconomic processes as well as settlement patterns of hunter-gatherer societies who occupied the Levant. Natufian sedentism and other aspects of the Natufian culture have received considerable attention (see papers in Bar-Yosef and Valla 1991). The wealth of information, however, is mainly derived from Early Natufian sites. The period of the Late Natufian sites (ca. 11,000–10,500 B.P.) is poorly known and such is the case with the Khiamian as well. The Harifian, a Late Natufian adaptation to the Negev and northern Sinai, is an exception. Even though many Early Neolithic sites have been excavated and published (Jericho [Kenyon 1981; Kenyon and Holland 1983], Nahal Oren [Stekelis and Yizraeli 1963; Noy et al. 1973], Gilgal I [Noy et al. 1980; Noy 1989], Gesher [Garfinkel and Nadel 1989], Iraq-ed-Dubb [Kuijt et al. 1991], Hatoula [Lechevallier and Ronen 1985; Lechevallier et al. 1989], and Netiv Hagdud [Bar-Yosef et al. 1980, 1991]) archaeobotanical and archaeozoological reports are few. This volume can thus make an important contribution in reconstructing Early Neolithic man-animal relationships and environmental aspects. We would like to thank the institutions and funding agencies that enabled us to carry out the field and laboratory research: the National Geographic Society, the Israel Academy of Sciences and Humanities, the Irene Levi Sala Care Archaeological

Foundation, the Institute of Archaeology of the Hebrew University, the Israel Exploration Society, and the Israel Prehistoric Society. We are especially grateful to the many individuals who took part in the field work, sometimes under strenuous conditions, especially D. Nadel, E. Hovers, Y. Garfinkel, and D. Enoch-Shiloh, as well as students from the Hebrew University and Tel Aviv University and volunteers from various countries. We wish to thank Professor Richard Meadow and Margot Fleischman of the Peabody Museum who helped in bringing this manuscript to publication.

Ofer Bar-Yosef and Avi Gopher

Contents

CHAPTER ONE

■

INTRODUCTION

■

CAN THE EARLY NEOLITHIC PEOPLE OF THE SOUTHERN LEVANT be considered precursors of all Old World farming communities? Was the phenomenon of domestication the inevitable result of Natufian sedentism? Did domestication emerge in southwest Asia as a direct consequence of the over-exploitation of the resources around early long-term habitations (Tchernov 1991a, 1991b)? Even after more than half a century of research in the Levant, evidence of the impetuses for farming and food production is lacking.

There should have been factors, other than the environmental-ecological ones, driving some human populations to initiate food production. These could have stemmed from a new and complex social structure, unknown before the emergence of Natufian sedentism, that was characterized by larger groups of people living together for extended periods, constrained by new social rules, immovable storage facilities, and the need to defend larger territories and immovable property. Indeed, the transition from a situation in which the population within a given area transformed itself spontaneously from bands of hunter-gatherers into larger societies of sedentary foragers is probably one of the best examples of an abrupt increase in the socioeconomic complexity of human beings.

The sedentary settlements and agricultural communities of the southern Levant developed out of an Epipaleolithic hunter-gatherer way of life (Braidwood 1975; Cauvin 1978; Henry 1983; Moore 1985; Bar-Yosef and Belfer-Cohen 1989; Henry 1989a; Hovers 1989; Hovers et al. 1988). Social and economic changes are clearly visible with the appearance of the Natufian entity when sedentism, the intensive harvesting of wild cereals, and storage came about. Bar-Yosef and Belfer-Cohen (1989) agree that the irreversible transformation of several families, extended families, or even small bands into complex social organizations led to the acquisition of new properties such as group identification, division of labor, and formation of task groups. How and why the complex Natufian Culture, essentially sedentary, emerged from a world of Kebaran hunter-gatherers is a fundamental question of human evolution.

A spontaneous increase in the organizational level of human communities at a certain place and time (Tchernov 1992) was also accompanied by a rapid increase in exploitation strategies and communication. However, sedentary communities survived in single localities over long periods, exploiting the same local resources over and over again, sometimes well into the Pre-Pottery Neolithic A (PPNA is used here only to designate a chronological period), without reaching the point of food production.

The Natufian entity emerged within a relatively limited area: from the Euphrates in the north (Moore 1989) to the Negev highlands in the south and the Jordanian Plateau in the east (Henry 1985, 1989a; Bar-Yosef and Belfer-Cohen 1989). Most of the Early and Middle Natufian sites (Valla 1987) have been found within the Mediterranean and Irano-Turanian phytogeographic regimes, with the core area being mainly along the oak-pistachio belt. The shift from an ephemeral and/or seasonal occupation by small groups to prolonged habitation by a relatively large community must have had a far reaching and profound impact on the proximate biotic environment, with the "Neolithic Revolution" being one of its ultimate consequences.

The importance of the Pre-Pottery Neolithic A lies in its comprising an intermediate or transitional phase between the Natufian period, which provides evidence for the earliest substantial sedentism of human beings (Bar-Yosef 1983; Henry 1989a; Bar-Yosef and Belfer-Cohen 1989; Tchernov 1991a, 1991b), and the expansion of farming communities which took place mainly within the Fertile Crescent in the Levant. Additionally, the PPNA provides us with the earliest evidence for cultivated wheat, barley, and legumes (D. Zohary and Hopf 1988; D. Zohary 1989). While these earliest beginnings of agriculture were undoubtedly important (at least in some of the sites) to the subsistence practices of the PPNA people, there is no way to estimate their quantitative or qualitative significance, as the PPNA people continued to gather wild plants and to hunt animals (Hillman et al. 1989; Tchernov and Horwitz 1991). The PPNA faunal assemblages are all dominated by gazelles (or gazelles and wild ibexes in southern Sinai, as at Abu Madi I). Domesticated sheep and goat were introduced to the southern Levant only during the Pre-Pottery Neolithic B (PPNB) period (Ducos 1968; Clutton-Brock 1981; Davis 1991).

The way to food production can be only understood in the light of the punctuated shift from small, simple human communities into ones with more complex social structures. While the unique place of the Natufian period in the history of human beings is marked by the swift adoption of social, technological, and subsistence innovations, it should be emphasized that increasing pressure by the occupants on their habitats forced them to look for completely different subsistence strategies. This included cultural control of wild gazelle populations (Horwitz et al. 1991; Cope 1991), and, as the biotic impoverishment increased as a result of local anthropogenic and global climatic impacts, specialized hunting practices (Tchernov 1991a, 1991b, 1992).

Evidently, a combination of swift climatic change to the colder and dryer period of the Younger Dryas during the eleventh millennium B.P. and the exhaustion of the biotic resources around the Natufian sites (Bar-Yosef and Belfer-Cohen 1989; Moore and Hillman 1992) had an immediate impact on human interaction with the environment in the Mediterranean belt of southwest Asia. This was expressed in behavioral and technological changes. These two factors could also be regarded as the main impetus for the Natufian people to move to more northern latitudes and to introduce Natufian lifeways to the Early Neolithic of northern Mesopotamia. In the southern Levant, however, the climatic change of the Younger Dryas caused some cultural and biotic impoverishment; the latest Natufian period in the Negev region was represented by a short-lived culture, the Harifian. It was only during the onset of wetter conditions around 10,300–10,000 B.P. that the expanding early Neolithic culture in the southern Levant showed an intensive use of wild and cultivated cereals, highly sophisticated hunting and gathering practices, as well as a continuation of the Natufian tradition of culling of male gazelles, as is shown at the site of Netiv Hagdud. The socioeconomic structure of PPNA societies was based on Natufian foundations with the addition of cultivation.

While the center of gravity of the social florescence during the Natufian period was centered on the limited Mediterranean zone of southwest Asia, the main center of activities of post-Natufian pre-farming societies was farther north. Indeed, Levantine PPNA sites are relatively limited in distribution and in number. The principal sites are as follows (fig. 1):

1. Mureybet (Cauvin 1977; Ducos 1978).
2. Nahal Oren (Stekelis and Yizraeli 1963; Noy et al. 1973).
3. Jericho (Kenyon 1981; Kenyon and Holland 1983; Clutton-Brock 1979).
4. Gilgal (Noy et al. 1980).
5. Netiv Hagdud (Bar-Yosef et al. 1980; Bar-Yosef et al. 1991).

6. Wadi Feidan (Bennet 1980).

7. Hatoula (Lechevallier and Ronen 1985, 1989).

8. Gesher (Garfinkel 1990).

9. Abu Madi I (Bar-Yosef 1985).

10. El Khiam Terrace (Echegaray 1966; Echegaray and Freeman 1989).

11. Salibiya IX (O. Bar-Yosef 1989).

12. Tell Aswad (Contenson 1983).

13. 'Iraq ed Dubb (Kuijt et al. 1991).

While the shift from small campsites of Epipaleolithic hunter-gatherers to larger Natufian base camps (occasionally exceeding 3000 m²) and eventually to villages is well recorded (Braidwood 1975; Moore 1985; Bar-Yosef and Belfer-Cohen 1989; Byrd 1992), the Early Neolithic, ca. 10,500–9,500 B.P., is less well-known due to the rarity of excavated sites (O. Bar-Yosef 1989). The few archaeological deposits known from this period are the lower layers of Jericho, originally called "Proto-Neolithic" and "Pre-Pottery Neolithic A" by Kenyon (1957) and now known as Sultanian (Crowfoot-Payne 1983); Phases II and III in the tell of Mureybet on the middle Euphrates River (Cauvin 1977); and the lowermost layer (Phase IA) in Tell Aswad (Contenson 1983) in the Damascus Basin. In the southern Levant, five additional sites have been discovered during the last decade, three in the Jordan River—Gilgal (Noy et al. 1980), Netiv Hagdud and Salibiya IX (O. Bar-Yosef 1989; Bar-Yosef et al. 1991), and Gesher (Garfinkel 1990)—and one, Hatoula, in the western foothills of Judea (Lechevallier and Ronen 1985). Abu Madi I, a PPNA site in southern Sinai, was excavated by Bar-Yosef (1985) and is currently under study. In Jordan, the cave site of 'Iraq ed Dubb is located on the eastern edge of the Mediterranean belt on the plateau of Wadi el Yabis, 550 m above sea level (Kuijt et al. 1991). It has been dated to 9,950 (±100) years B.P.

The onset of the Early Neolithic in the southern Levant can be placed around 10,300–10,200 B.P. (based on dated wood, mainly *Tamarix*) (Cauvin 1987). The radiocarbon dates for Phase II of Mureybet range from 10,500 to 10,000 B.P. There is no evidence for simultaneous onset of the Neolithic in the northern and southern Levant (O. Bar-Yosef 1989; Bar-Yosef and Belfer-Cohen 1991).

Cauvin (1989) argues that the neolithization process in the Levant, which occurred earlier than in other regions, provides interesting data for a comparative analysis with other areas of the world. The appearance of agriculture at about 10,000 B.P. shows the importance of the roles played not only by ecological conditions but also by the lengthy processes of sociological and cultural maturation that started with Natufian sedentism and led humans to food production. Neolithization for Cauvin (1989) appears as a progressive and overall transformation, in which food production may be regarded as the consequence of a cultural and mental change rather than of other (physical) parameters. This process began in a very limited area ("critical zone") comprising a corridor extending from the Jordan to the Middle Euphrates Valley (Bar-Yosef and Belfer-Cohen 1989), situated at the intersection of the nuclear zone of wild cereals and the cultural zone of Natufian and Khiamian hunter-gatherers, where specific technologies of the Neolithic economy had developed (Zohary and Hopf 1988).

The shift from the Natufian to the Early Neolithic took place around 10,300 B.P. (Bar-Yosef and Belfer-Cohen 1991) with the emergence of the large Early Neolithic communities (Cauvin 1987; O. Bar-Yosef 1989) that were associated with either cultivated or intensively collected wild barley. In addition, exploitation of other vegetal resources (various legumes, oats, acorns, pistachio nuts, and figs) seems to have greatly increased (Kislev et al. 1986; Kislev and Bar-Yosef 1988; Zohary and Hopf 1988), while the exploitation of animal resources seems to have continued the Natufian tradition of specialized hunting of diverse vertebrates, including many small species of mammals, birds, and reptiles (Tchernov 1991b). However, it should be taken into account that the state of preservation of vegetal remains from Natufian deposits is rather poor in comparison to the PPNA sites, and this may bias our results and conclusions.

Can food production in the Old World be considered monophyletic from an evolutionary point of view? Or was each of the early domesticates taken into cultivation many times ("the multiple events model," Zohary 1989)? While the biological mechanisms of domestication may be considered more objectively, its earlier stages are far from fully understood. Cytological observations are compatible with the model of a single domestication event for the founder crops in the Near East, i.e., all the early domesticated plants in the Palearctic region are monophyletic (Zohary 1989). On the other hand, early animal husbandry either could have been polyphyletic or could have occurred several times in different locations from different wild stocks.

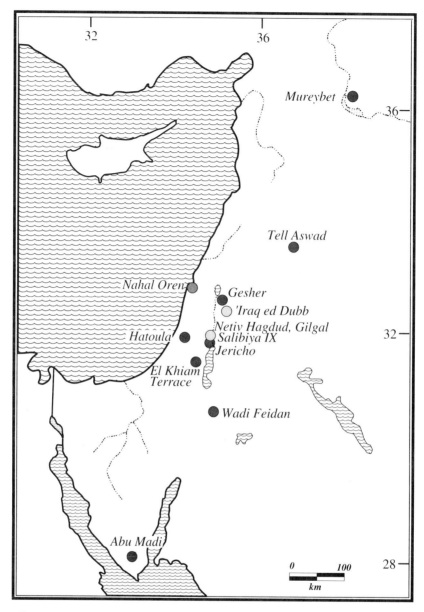

Figure 1
Location of principal PPNA sites in the southern Levant.

Ecologically it has often been stressed that all PPNA sites were located in proximity to permanent bodies of water (O. Bar-Yosef 1989). Yet it should also be emphasized that most of these sites were distributed along the southeastern Levantine arid to semiarid zone. Both the need for permanent sources of water and the ecological richness of these special biotopes could have dictated the location of the PPNA settlements. These oases-like isolates may be considered biogeographically as tropical enclaves, or relicts, isolated within the southern Palearctic deserts (Tchernov 1988). In these wetter isolates species diversity and biomass would have been conspicuously higher than in the surrounding regions, as is seen today in all oases of the Saharo-Arabian arid belt, and therefore would have been the only places that could have supported larger settlements.

O. Bar-Yosef (1989) has mentioned that each of the PPNA settlements where cultivation was practiced is located either very near to or on alluvial soils. He argued that this situation enabled the people to exploit land that was renewed by layers of seasonally accumulated sediments. Thus, these enclaves of alluvial soils were not only ecologically richer in species diversity and biomass, but enabled better growth of trees within the arid or semiarid regions. Some of these trees, like the fig, could have been used as significant sources of food (Kislev in Bar-Yosef et al. 1991).

It is thus the transition from the Natufian period to the PPNA that marks the onset of the Neolithic Revolution, just one stage before the distribution of plant cultivation and animal domestication in the Levant during the PPNB, that makes the PPNA sites of such importance. This socioeconomic revolution brought about the reliance of human societies on systematic cultivation of a suite of plants (the founder crops) and the daily tending and herding of goat, sheep, cattle, and pigs. This reconstruction is therefore based on available plant remains and animal bones. While there is more information on the plant remains of the Early Neolithic sites of the Middle Euphrates (Mureybet) and the Damascus Basin (Tell Aswad; Zeist and Bakker-Heeres 1985, 1986), the basic data set for the Early Neolithic of the southern Levant is still scanty (O. Bar-Yosef 1989; Bar-Yosef et al. 1991).

No complete faunal list has yet been established for the southern Levantine PPNA. Therefore, this transitional period has remained poorly understood compared to the Late Natufian and PPNB in terms of detailed biotic reconstruction of its paleocommunities, paleoecological implications, and changes in animal exploitation and subsistence. The relative rarity of PPNA sites in this region has also kept us from substantial knowledge of this period. Animal life and the structural features of the habitats in the southern Levant at the end of the Pleistocene and the beginning of the Holocene were still very different than in the latest Neolithic and Chalcolithic, but no reconstruction of the biota of this crucial period has ever been seriously attempted. The relatively rich fauna of Netiv Hagdud opens a wider window into this particularly crucial period, and provides an opportunity to better understand the ecological picture of the Lower Jordan Valley. A species list for Netiv Hagdud, with information on relative frequencies and spatial and temporal distributions, will fill a long-existing gap in the biochronology from the Epipaleolithic to the Neolithic in the southern Levant.

Because of its ecological and biogeographical location within the Lower Jordan Valley, north of the Dead Sea, Netiv Hagdud plays an important role. Shortly after the PPNA this region underwent conspicuous geological, climatological, paleoenvironmental, and cultural changes (Tchernov 1988). Ecologically, Netiv Hagdud is located at present well within the desert vegetational belt with a typical Arabian (Tchernov 1988), or desert fauna (Werner 1988). The flora is defined as Saharo-Arabian (Danin 1988), with impoverished diffused communities of *Zygophyllum*, *Suaeda*, *Gymnocarpus*, etc. (See Part I). It is thus also important to offer logical explanations for the dominance of typical Mediterranean elements in this area some 9,500 years ago.

■

CHAPTER TWO

ARCHAEOLOGY, MATERIAL, AND METHODS

■

THE EXCAVATIONS THAT WERE CARRIED OUT IN NETIV HAG-dud yielded reasonably large quantities of well-pre-served faunal assemblages that proved to be extreme-ly informative. The Early Neolithic village of Netiv Hagdud was systematically excavated by Bar-Yosef over three seasons (1983, 1984, 1986). During this period an area of about 500 m² on the western side of the mound (Upper Area) and a deep sounding on the northern edge of the mound were uncovered. The archaeology and a preliminary list of the plants and animals from this site have already been published in some detail (Bar-Yosef et al. 1991) and more complete reports are to be found in Bar-Yosef and Gopher (1994)—Part I of this site report. The reader will find most of the necessary data concerning the history, the stratigraphy, the burials, and the structures in that publication.

A schematic section of the Deep Sounding is given in figure 2. This section was taken, with modifica-tions, from Bar-Yosef et al. (1991) and Bar-Yosef and Gopher (1994), in order to show the stratigraphic subdivisions of the faunal assemblages in relation to the sequence of the Deep Sounding. Following the division of this section into three complexes (Lower, Middle, and Upper), the faunal assemblages were accordingly divided and analyzed. This section also indicates the position of the radiocarbon dates throughout the sequence. It is worth noting that in general the quality of preservation of plants and ani-mals in the deposits gradually increased with depth, so that below 1 m from the surface the bones of even the most delicate passeriform bird could be retrieved in excellent condition. Except for in the Upper Area, the bones were usually devoid of any calcareous encrustation. In general, the state of preservation throughout the sequence was excellent.

The volume of the excavated material from the Upper Area and from the three complexes of the Deep Sounding is given in table 1 (for more details see also Bar-Yosef et al. 1991 and Bar-Yosef and Gopher 1994). Obviously most of the excavated material derived from the Upper Area, while the Deep Sounding area supplies a more complete picture of the faunal succes-sion at the site. The calculation of the amount of exca-vated material enabled us to compare the number of bones per unit of excavated volume (bone density).

The two widely employed and discussed methods for quantifying zooarchaeological assemblages are Number of Identified Specimens (NISP) and Mini-mum Number of Individuals (MNI) (Klein and Cruz-

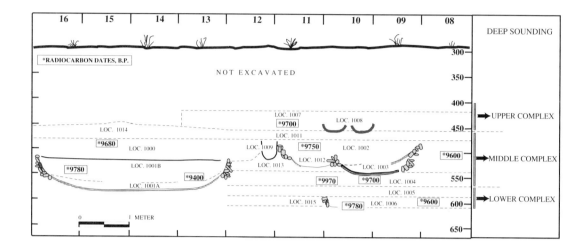

Figure 2
A schematic section of the Deep Sounding of Netiv Hagdud, showing the stratigraphic subdivision of the faunal assemblages along the sequence. Modified after Bar-Yosef et al. 1991.

Uribe 1984). The chief drawback to using MNI for fossil samples is the over-representation of rare species, which results in artificial species evenness in these samples. In many cases we followed Grayson (1984), who recommended the use of NISP as a basic measure of taxonomic abundance in archaeological faunas. The MNI in each layer was determined by counting the most common element of each taxon. Relative abundance was determined on the basis of these numbers. Skeletal material recovered from the sequence was combined by layers, or areas, and MNI was calculated for each of these. Counts and minimum numbers were adjusted to compensate for variation in the volumes excavated fill.

It has been shown (Bar-Yosef et al. 1991; Bar-Yosef and Gopher 1994) that intrasettlement variability resulted from the presence of specialized or localized activities. Different activity areas hold the potential for deciphering aspects of the social hierarchy through the identification of households, dumping areas, and public activity areas. However, analysis of the distribution of faunal remains failed to show any special localities for specific fauna-related activities in the site, instead showing only different densities of bone deposition. Imported raw materials and goods, such as obsidian, marine shells (D. E. Bar-Yosef 1989, 1991), and greenstone beads hint at the presence of exchange networks among the inhabitants. Perishable items may have been exchanged as well, but they did not leave any traces in the archaeological record. As for animals and plants, except for marine shells,

no signs of trade or exchange can be claimed; all food sources originated from the near surroundings of the site. Nor is it possible to show differences in the distribution of species or quantities of animal remains between structures and burials. The 95 marine shells from Netiv Hagdud (D. E. Bar-Yosef 1991) were brought from both the Red Sea and the Mediterranean. In comparison with Natufian marine shell assemblages it seems that cowries (Cypraeidae) and *Glycimeris* had now begun to play a more important role in decoration (D. E. Bar-Yosef 1989). At the site of Hatoula, however, Mediterranean fish remains (*Sparus*) were recovered (Davis 1985), indicating that some sort of food was also imported by the local inhabitants.

A R E A	m³	%
UPPER AREA	123.9	84.80
DEEP SOUNDING　　a. Upper Complex	3.0	2.05
b. Middle Complex	12.7	8.70
c. Lower Complex	6.5	4.45
Total	146.1	100

Table 1.
Volumes excavated from Netiv Hagdud (Bar-Yosef et al. 1991). All counts of skeletal material (MNI, NISP) were adjusted to compensate for variation in the volumes of excavated fill.

■

CHAPTER THREE

SYSTEMATIC PALEONTOLOGY

■

MOLLUSCA

An extensive molluscan fauna was recovered from throughout the sequence of the site. These remains originated from three different ecological units:

Terrestrial Snails

This group was naturally deposited or accidentally introduced into the mound and thus may reflect the environmental and depositional conditions that prevailed during that period. In spite of the ability of some of the species to penetrate the sediment, they never dig more than 20–25 cm below the surface, and therefore their sequential deposition along the section is not affected. In terms of numbers of animals (but not biomass), the land snails constitute a major component of the fauna, but have not yet been identified and studied. No traces have been found to show that people used this protein-rich resource for food. The only large and reasonably edible terrestrial snail which existed in the area during this period is *Helix*; it is found only occasionally through the sequence and seems to have been left untouched. The remaining species are much smaller.

Marine Shells

This group is surprisingly scarce (less than 100 specimens) throughout the sequence. It has been studied by D. E. Bar-Yosef (1989) (also summarized in table 3 in Bar-Yosef et al. 1991). The relatively limited number of species was collected from both the Red Sea and the Mediterranean coasts.

Freshwater Molluscs

Over 800 specimens were uncovered, and all of them (except one, see below) were identified as *Melanopsis praemorsa* (Olivier, 1801) (Gastropoda, Thiaridae). This species appears in a great variety of ecotypes and wide range of morphotypes throughout eastern Mediterranean freshwater bodies (Tchernov 1973, 1975a), and thus may be used as an indicator of the presence of freshwater habitats during the PPNA period in this region. As some of the abiotic factors, like salinity of water, are directly reflected in the structure and morphology of the shell (Tchernov 1975b), some of these morphotypes are considered as unique species. Populations with smooth shells usually occupy springs and slow running streams of low salinity. Moderately and irregularly keeled shells can be found in highly saline waters. Strongly and regularly keeled morphotypes are able to inhabit open lakes and survive turbulent open waters (Tchernov 1975b). Schütt (1983) preferred to designate the smooth form as *Melanopsis praemorsa ferussaci*; others, like Mienis (1983), as *Melanopsis praemorsa buccinoidea*. The elongated and the semi-costated form, which is also known from the Lower Jordan Valley, has been called *Melanopsis cerithiopsis* by Mienis (1983).

All three morphotypes (or species?) are found throughout the sequence of Netiv Hagdud. This may indicate the existence of a large variety of water sources with differing chemical constituents (more or less oligohaline) and open water bodies that could have been quite turbulent. In order to simplify the partitioning of the ecological units, we divided the *Melanopsis* assemblages into two complexes—smooth and costated—that show a clear demarcation respectively between genuine turbulent freshwater bodies and springs and streams. Some idea of the abundance of *Melanopsis* remains and their relative and absolute frequencies in the mound and through the sequence is given in table 2. Although there are no significant changes through time, numerically most of the shells were uncovered from the Upper Area. In relation to excavated volume, however, they are significantly more abundant in the Middle Complex of the Deep Sounding area. The proportions of the two ecotypes, smooth versus costated, vary only modestly through the sequence and are statistically insignificant. Given that the accumulation of *Melanopsis* in the deposits

was most probably caused by humans bringing in clays for the production of mud-brick or adobe walls, the presence of more than 50 percent of the costated morph indicates that a significant body of water existed near the site during this period.

A single specimen of *Unio terminalis* Bourguignat, 1857 (Bivalvia, Unionidae) was retrieved from the Upper Area. This species, which regularly occupies genuine water bodies, is absent at present from the region. However, this specimen could have been artificially introduced into the site from another region.

The most common freshwater mollusc in the southern Levant is undoubtedly *Theodoxus jordani* (Sowerby, 1836) (Neritidae, Gastropoda). Of all other freshwater molluscs, this extremely euryohaline species occupies the widest range of continental waters, and at present is abundant in practically all the water bodies around the Dead Sea and in the Lower Jordan Valley. Its conspicuous absence from the site is astonishing, particularly in light of the fact that this species has been recovered from early Holocene (post-Lisan) non-anthropological deposits all along the Lower Jordan Valley (unpublished data) a few km north of Netiv Hagdud. Its total absence from the site, as well as from the nearby PPNA site of Gilgal (Noy et al. 1980), demands an explanation which we do not have. We can suggest only that either the species was indeed absent from the area at the end of the Pleistocene, and thus may be regarded as a Holocene invader, or else was selectively eliminated by predators and/or people.

| COMPLEX | DEEP SOUNDING | | | | | | UPPER AREA | | | |
| | LOWER COMPLEX | | MIDDLE COMPLEX | | UPPER COMPLEX | | | | TOTAL | |
Ecotype	Smooth	Costated	Smooth	Costated	Smooth	Costated	Smooth	Costated	Smooth	Costated
Number of Specimens	26	40	142	114	5	11	161	325	334	490
Frequency (%) in Complex	39.4	60	55.46	54.54	32.25	68.75	33.13	66.87		
Frequency (%) in Site	7.78	8.16	42.51	23.27	1.50	2.24	48.20	66.33		
Absolute Abundance (per m 3)	4.00	6.15	11.18	8.97	1.66	3.66	1.29	2.62		
							Grand Total		**824**	

Table 2
Relative and absolute representation of the freshwater snail *Melanopsis praemorsa* (Thiaridae, Gastropoda) along the sequence of Netiv Hagdud. The *Melanopsis* assemblage was divided into two well-defined morphotypes (or different species, see text), each of which may have occupied different types of water bodies.

ARTHROPODA

Crustacea

Numerous remains (mainly chelipeds) of the fresh-water crab *Potamon fluviatilis* (Decapoda, Brachyura) are present throughout the layers. Currently, this species is widespread in all varieties of water bodies in the southern Levant. Its home range is fairly large, and during humid nights its foraging territory may extend even to 70 m from its underwater roosting sites. Crabs could easily have found their way into the habitation site where they foraged for food, much as they do today in camp sites. Their origin in the deposits could be natural, or the crabs could also have been retrieved by humans, small carnivores, birds of prey, or storks. In any event, their abundance in the deposits reinforces the evidence for the proximity of a variety of water bodies to Netiv Hagdud.

VERTEBRATA

Teleostei

A few vertebrae, scales, and a pharyngeal arch of bony fish were found in the Middle Complex of the Deep Sounding. The rather scarce remains were not identified but seem to have come from a small-size fresh-water Cypriniform that could have occupied springs and other water bodies in the vicinity of the site. At present larger species of Cyprinidae (like representatives of the genus *Barbus*) are known from some of the larger springs along the Lower Jordan Valley and around the Dead Sea.

Much as with the land snails, the remains of only small-sized species suggest that there was no reliance on fish as a protein source. It is worth noting that no fish remains were found in the nearby site of Gilgal (Noy et al. 1980). In layers 2 and 3 of Hatoula (early PPNA), however, vertebrae of much larger fish (20–25 cm) were found and identified as *Sparus auratus* (the sea bream), a typical Mediterranean species (Sparidae) (Davis 1985).

Amphibia

Anura

Ranidae
Rana ridibunda Pallas, 1771
A few limb bones and a single sacral vertebra of Anurans, all of which have been identified as *Rana ridibunda* (table 3), are present mainly in the Middle Complex. This species is still common in some of the springs around the Dead Sea area and the Lower Jordan Valley (Mendelssohn and Steinitz 1944).

As this frog will not forage outside water, it seems that its deposition in the site was either anthropogenic or was caused by birds (storks, herons) or other predators. Amphibians have not been recovered from Hatoula (Davis 1985), but a few vertebrae of Anurans were identified from the site of Gilgal (Noy et al. 1980).

The scarcity of this edible frog from the site of Netiv Hagdud reinforces our impression that aquatic elements did not play any role in the diet of the local inhabitants.

Reptilia

Lacertilia

Chameleonidae
Chameleo chameleon Linnaeus, 1758
Bones of the most abundant lizard (table 3) in the faunal assemblage, *Chameleo chameleon*, were retrieved from throughout the Deep Sounding. The well-preserved lower jaws enabled us to reach a specific identification. In the future, further detailed morphological and biometric comparisons will make it possible to attribute the chameleon population of Netiv Hagdud to one of the two subspecies which occur at present in the southern Levant (Werner 1988). *Chameleo chameleon rectristricta* Boettger, 1880, is confined to the Mediterranean zone and Mount Hermon, never below the 250–300 mm rainfall isohyet. *Chameleo chameleon musae* (Steindachner, 1900) is an isolated relict form found in the southern coastal dunes of Israel and northern Sinai, where it could have been cut off from the main Mediterranean stock of chameleons during the post-Glacial (Tchernov 1981).

AREA	DEEP	SOUNDING		UPPER AREA	Total
Complex Species	Lower Complex	Middle Complex	Upper Complex		
Amphibia					
Rana ridibunda	-	2 - ilium(c)(l+r)	-	-	2
Rana ridibunda	-	2 - Humeri (c)(l)	-	-	2
Rana ridibunda	1 - Sacral Vertebra	-	-	-	1
Rana ridibunda	-	2 - Tibio-fibula (c)(r)	-	-	2
Rana ridibunda	-	1 - Metatarsus (c)(l)	-	-	1
Reptilia		-	-	-	
Ophidia	(36 Vertebrae)	(196 Vertebrae)	(32 Vertebrae)	(6 Vertebrae)	(+270)
Chameleo chameleon	-	2 - Pterygoideum (c)	-	-	2
Chameleo chameleon	-	2 - Lower Jaws(c)(l+r)	-	-	2
Chameleo chameleon	-	2 - Lower Jaws (i)(r+l)	-	-	2
Chameleo chameleon	-	1 - Lower Jaw (i)(r)	-	-	1
Chameleo chameleon	1 - Maxillary (i)(l)	-	-	-	1
Ophisaurus apodus	-	-	8 - Vertebrae	-	8
Ophisaurus apodus	-	6 - Vertebrae	-	-	1
Ophisaurus apodus	-	1 - Lower Jaw (i)(r)	-	-	1
Ophisaurus apodus	-	-	1 - Pterygoideum (i)	-	1
Ophisaurus apodus	1 - Lower Jaw (i)(l)	-	-	-	1
Ophisaurus apodus	-	1 -Parietal (c)	-	-	1
Agama stellio	-	-	1 - Lower Jaw (i)(l)	-	1
Agama stellio	-	-	1 - Lower Jaw (i)(r)	-	1
Agama stellio	-	2 - Lower Jaw (c)(r+l)	-	-	2
Lacerta trilineata	-	1 - Lower Jaw (i)(l)	-	-	1
Lacerta trilineata	-	-	1 - Lower Jaw (i)(l)	-	1
Testudo graeca	-	1 - Femur (c)(l)	-	-	1
Lacertidae (genus undet.)	-	2 - Vertebrae	-	-	2
Lacertidae (genus undet.)	-	-	1 - Parietal (c)	-	1
Lacertidae (genus undet.)	-	-	1 - Lower Jaw (i)(l)	-	1
Lacertidae (genus undet.)	-	1 - Femur (c)(r)	-	-	1
Lacertidae (genus undet.)	-	-	1 - Maxillary (i)(l)	-	1

Table 3
Inventory of the herpetofaunal remains from Netiv Hagdud.
c=complete; i=incomplete; l=left; r=right;(+)=ophidian vertebrae.

Agamidae

Agama stellio Linnaeus, 1758
This is the next most common lizard (table 3) and was mainly identified from well-preserved jaws. This species essentially occupies Mediterranean habitats and does not exist at present in the area of Netiv Hagdud. *Agama stellio brachydactyla* Haas, 1951, occurs in small isolates in the more mesic mountainous regions of the southern Levant as a glacial relict (Tchernov 1981).

Anguidae

Ophisaurus apodus Pallas, 1772
Relatively common in the herpetofaunal record, this species was easily identified by well-preserved jaws, characteristic vertebrae, and a single pterygoideum (table 3). This legless lizard inhabits Mediterranean maquis and shrub landscapes and usually avoids areas with mean annual rainfall less than 400 mm.

Lacertidae

Lacerta trilineata Betriga, 1886
This species was identified from two well-preserved lower jaws from the Deep Sounding. It is a typical inhabitant of Mediterranean woods and shrubs and is not found at present south of the Galilee region.

Other remains of lacertilians were not identifiable to species level, but generally seem to have come from individuals in the above list of species. It is worth noting that neither the most common lizard in the Lower Jordan Valley and the Dead Sea area at present, *Mesalina guttulata*, nor any other recent local reptiles are present in the herpetofaunal list. It is astonishing that none of the PPNA lizard community of Netiv

Hagdud survived the beginning of the Holocene in this area.

Ophidia

Numerous vertebrae (table 3) were recovered from the sequence, but no attempt was made to identify the material to lower taxonomic categories. The positive and high correlation between the length, width, and height of ophidian vertebrae with body length made it possible to extrapolate and evaluate the size of Netiv Hagdud snakes. These indicated body lengths ranging between 75 and 125 cm.

Testudines

Testudinidae
Testudo graeca Forskal, 1775
A single specimen of *Testudo graeca* was identified from a femur. This species, which probably includes two different subspecies in the southern Levant, is chiefly confined to Mediterranean landscapes and is currently absent from the region of Netiv Hagdud.

A comparison of the herpetofaunal assemblages of Netiv Hagdud with those from the early PPNA of Hatoula (Judea) and Gilgal (Lower Jordan Valley) (Bar-Yosef and Belfer-Cohen 1989) shows that in both of the latter sites the remains of reptiles are relatively very scarce (Davis 1985; Noy et al. 1980). This discrepancy is either due to poor recovery techniques or to the actual absence of reptiles in the assemblages. The species composition of Netiv Hagdud remains indicates that most of the reptiles belong to large-size forms: especially *Ophisaurus apodus*, most of the snakes, and *Testudo graeca*. It does not seem likely that the remains of these species were regurgitated or deposited in the site by birds of prey or other predators. Reptiles clearly were an important food resource, although the protein biomass represented by this group is relatively low.

It is also worth noting that limb bones were the main elements retrieved from amphibians. However, no lacertilian limb bones were recovered from the site, except for one femur of an unidentified lizard, along with remains of cranial elements.

Aves

Avifaunal remains, in terms of both species diversity and numbers of individuals, are surprisingly abundant. Unfortunately, except for the short analysis of the bird remains from Gilgal (Tchernov in Noy et al. 1980), no other PPNA avifaunal assemblage from the southern Levant has yet been published. While Blandermar and Cowles (British Museum, Tring, Hartforshire) studied the birds of Jericho, they never published their results. They were kind enough to allow us to use their list of birds from Jericho, however, so we could compare it with the birds of Netiv Hagdud. Incomplete information from other contemporary sites keeps us from a better understanding of the general attitude of the PPNA people toward this important resource. As a highly diversified group, the habitat partitioning of birds is finely shaped and relatively well demarcated. Birds faithfully reflect the immediate environment, and therefore they may be effectively used for reconstructing the ancient habitats around the site. Paleoecological comparison with other sites is at present restricted to a very few sites.

The list of birds recovered shows a relatively wide spectrum of species of different sizes and reflects a mosaic of habitats around the site. To hunt such a large variety of species demanded extensive experience as well as the use of different techniques. In this respect it seems that the PPNA people continued the Natufian tradition and possibly elaborated on it.

Due to the special biogeographical position of Netiv Hagdud on the principal Afro-Eurasian migration route, it was expected that some of the migrants would be represented in the site. Indeed, a wide array of species from many different habitats and including both residents and migratory species is represented in the assemblage. Discussion of their general and local distribution, the nature of their habitats, their feeding behaviors, and the local status of each one of the birds that were identified at this site is presented in some detail below, as the reconstruction of the ancient habitats and the interpretation of paleoecological conditions in the Lower Jordan Valley during this period relies heavily on this information.

Charadriiformes

Burhinidae

Burhinus oedicnemus (Linnaeus, 1758)

The stone-curlew is Eurasian and North African and is found in Mediterranean, steppe, mild temperate, and arid zones with mainly a continental climate. This species' habitat preference ranges from heathland to stony plateau, tablelands, extensive sand dunes, and saline tracts (including river banks, streams, lakes, and lagoons). It is primarily a ground bird and partly nocturnal. Its diet is chiefly composed of terrestrial invertebrates and small vertebrates. The southern Palearctic populations of this species (*Burhinus oedicnemus saharae*) are resident in the southern Levant. Northern forms (such as *Burhinus oedicnemus oedicnemus*) may appear as migrants. Bone material is confined to one humerus retrieved from the Middle Complex (table 4).

Charadriidae

Hoplopterus spinosus (Linnaeus, 1758)

The spur-winged plover or lapwing has an Eastern Mediterranean and Afrotropical pattern of distribution. It breeds and feeds chiefly on insects usually near surface waters in open marshy places or by lakes, lagoons, and riversides. In the Levant, populations of *Hoplopterus spinosus* are dispersives or residents, occasionally wintering in the Mediterranean areas. Relative to other non-passeriform birds, this species is fairly abundant in the fossil record of Netiv Hagdud, and its bones were mainly recovered from the Middle Complex (table 4).

Gruiformes

Rallidae

Fulica atra Linnaeus, 1758

The coot has a Eurasiatic and Australian distribution and prefers fairly shallow, organically-rich, muddy bottom waters, with room to dive and with ample marginal, emergent, floating, or bottom vegetation.

AREA	D E E P	S O U N D I N G		UPPER AREA	TOTAL
Complex	Lower Complex	Middle Complex	Upper Complex		
Species					
Charadriiformes					
Burhinus oedicnemus	-	1-Humerus (p)(r)	-	-	1
Hoplopterus spinosus	-	2-Humerus (p)(l+r)	-	-	2
Hoplopterus spinosus	-	3-Coracoid (c)(l+2r)	-	-	3
Hoplopterus spinosus	-	2-Coracoid(d)(r)	-	-	2
Hoplopterus spinosus	-	1-Tibia (d)(l)	-	-	1
Hoplopterus spinosus	-	1-Sternum (p)	-	-	1
Gruiformes					
Fulica atra	-	1-Coracoid (d)(l)	-	-	1
Otis tarda	1-Coracoid (p)(r)	1-Phalanx 1 (Digit II,Wing)(c)		1-Phalanx 1 (Digit II,Wing)(c)	3
Columbiformes					
Columba livia	-	1-Sternum (p)	-	-	1
Columba livia	-	1-Scapula (c)(r)	-	-	1
Streptopelia decaocto	1-Carpometacarpus(p)(l)	1-Ulna (c)(r)	1-Coracoid (c)(r)	-	3
Streptopelia decaocto	-	1-Humerus (p)(l)	-	-	1
Streptopelia decaocto	-	2-Coracoid (c)(r+l)	-	-	2
Streptopelia decaocto	-	1-Coracoid (p)(r)	-	-	1
Streptopelia decaocto	-	1-Scapula (p)(?)	-	-	1
Ciconiiformes					
Ciconia ciconia	1-Sternum (p)	1-Coracoid (c)(l)	1-Phalanx 1(Digit II,Wing)(c)(?)	-	3
Ciconia ciconia	-	2-Coracoid (p)(l)	-	-	2
Ciconia ciconia	-	2-Coracoid (d)(r+l)	-	-	2
Ciconia ciconia	-	1-Carpometacarpus (p)(r)	-	-	1
Ciconia ciconia	-	1-Carpometacarpus (d)(l)	-	-	1
Ciconia ciconia	-	1-Ulna (i)(?)	-	-	1
Ciconia ciconia	-	1-Femur (d)(l)	-	-	1
Ciconia ciconia	-	1-Tibia (p)(l)	-	-	1
Ciconia ciconia	-	1-Tarsometatarsus (p)(r)	-	-	1
Ciconia ciconia	-	2-Tarsometatarsus (d)(l+r)	-	-	2
Ciconia ciconia	-	1-Phalanx 1 (Digit II, Foot (c)	-	-	1
Ciconia ciconia	-	1-Humerus (p)(l)	-	-	1
Ciconia ciconia	-	1-Scapula (p)(?)	-	-	1
Leptoptilos crumeniferus	-	1- Coracoid (p)(r)	-	-	1
Total	**3**	**37**	**2**	**1**	**43**

Table 4
Inventory of bird remains, representation of their skeletal elements, and their distribution along the sequence.
c=complete; i= incomplete; d=distal; p= proximal; l= left; r= right; ?= side unknown.

Essentially an omnivore, this bird prefers vegetative parts of seeds of aquatic and sometimes terrestrial plants, including debris drifting on the surface. At present a transient and wintering bird in the southern Levant, occasional breeders have also been recorded. The record from Netiv Hagdud is confined to one coracoid (table 4).

Otididae

Otis tarda Linnaeus, 1758

A mainly southern and central Palearctic species, the great bustard occupies lowland habitats, river valleys, and undulating open country. It avoids areas liable to receive annual rainfall much above 600 mm as well as forests, wetlands, deserts, and rocky terrain and feeds on invertebrates, small vertebrates, and plants. Dispersive and resident in the northern Levant, it is chiefly observed on semiarid plateaus but is absent today from the southern Levantine region. A few remains (table 4) were uncovered from the Lower and Middle Complex and the Upper Area.

Ciconiiformes

Ciconiidae

Leptoptilos crumeniferus (Lesson, 1831)

An Afrotropical bird, in 1951 and 1957 this species was recorded from the Hulleh Valley and Lake Tiberias. Marabou may be migratory, partially migratory, and dispersive. Known chiefly as carrion eaters, individuals may forage for long distances. They may also feed on a large variety of small vertebrates and large insects, mainly locusts.

Marabou may belong to a tropical vagrant group (like *Porphyria porphyria* or *Ardea goliath*) which mainly includes wetland species that are able to travel along the Nile and reach the eastern Mediterranean region (Yom-Tov 1988). Yet, many Afrotropical elements, large non-vagrant species, as well as small birds were, and still are, an integral component of the southern Levantine biota (Tchernov 1988). The marabou of Netiv Hagdud either constitutes a representative of a late relict Afrotropical (Ethiopian) component in the Jordan Valley, where many other species still survive, or is an accidental vagrant.

One coracoid (table 4) was retrieved from the Middle Complex.

Ciconia ciconia (Linnaeus, 1758)

A trans-Palearctic species (mid-latitude continental and Mediterranean climates), the white stork has dis-

persed during the last centuries into a rather patchy pattern of distribution. Preferring open wetlands, floodlands, moist meadows, or arable fields, as well as all kinds of freshwater habitats for feeding, it consumes different kinds and sizes of vertebrates and invertebrates. For breeding it uses tall trees and (for partially commensal populations) lofty human-made perches. Most of the white storks seen in southwest Asia belong to the nominate subspecies *C. c. ciconia*. Occasionally it breeds in the southern Levant.

The Levant is one of the principal migration routes for the eastern European populations. The eastern (Rift Valley) route for the spring migration may channel many thousands of storks per day on their way northward. Yet, it is also possible, as with many other Palearctic elements until the end of the Pleistocene, that the breeding belt of the white stork included much lower latitudes, and resident populations still could have occurred in the Jordan Valley during the PPNA period (Tchernov 1981, 1988; Pichon 1984).

Among the non-passeriform bird remains of Netiv Hagdud, the white stork is one of the most abundant species (table 4), but its bones are mainly confined to the Middle Complex of the Deep Sounding area. Table 5 represents a comparison between the few measurable skeletal elements of the fossil assemblage with a few recent individuals. Although most of the recent specimens are clearly smaller, there are too few specimens for any statistical assessment.

Columbiformes

Columbidae

Columba livia Gmelin, 1789

Although its original distribution is obscure, the rock dove seems to have been predominantly a trans-Palearctic species. It occupies an extreme variety of climatic zones, but nest sites are almost always (a stenotopic species) on rock faces, mainly in cliffs, caves, and closed rock ledges. Feral and commensal populations have successfully transformed these sites in anthropogenic habitats and within human settlements into suitable alternative nest sites. It is essentially a graminivorous species.

Feral and less-contaminated populations are very common all over the southern Levantine region, covering Mediterranean landscapes as successfully as desolate desert escarpments, but daily access to water is obligatory. This species was described from the early Pleistocene deposits of the 'Ubeidiya Formation

Variables	98-S-8 540-550	28-T-8 520	98-R-16 490-500	L-1007 R-13	98-T-8 540-550	98-R-8 530-540	Recent	Recent	Recent	Recent	Recent
Carpomatacarpus											
Total length	119.73	-	-	-	-	-	113.84	111.60	115.79	-	-
Width of distal end	20.13	-	-	-	-	-	18.15	18.00	18.44	-	-
Width of proximal end	25.06	-	-	-	-	-	23.32	23.51	24.29	-	-
Diameter of trochlea	10.23	-	-	-	-	-	10.29	10.60	10.63	-	-
Tarsometatarsus											
Width of proximal end	-	19.27	-	-	-	-	-	-	-	-	-
Width of distal end	-	-	21.03	-	-	-	-	-	-	-	-
Phalanx 1, wing digit II											
Maximal length	-	-	-	50.72	-	-	44.17	-	44.69	-	-
Femur											
Maximal width of distal end	-	-	-	-	23.31	-	21.87	23.36	23.94	23.61	22.35
Tibiotarsus											
Maximal width of proximal end	-	-	-	-	-	27.33	-	-	-	-	-

Table 5

Measurements of *Ciconia ciconia* from Netiv Hagdud compared with some recent specimens. All the measurements of the recent individuals are smaller, but there are too few to draw a conclusion.

(Tchernov 1980), showing the great antiquity of the species in the southern Levantine province.

Records of the rock dove are confined to two specimens derived from the Middle Complex (table 4).

Streptopelia decaocto Frivaldszky, 1838

The original distribution of the collared dove is obscure due either to historical and recent large-scale expansion or to recent genetic changes. The argument that the original area of the species is the Levantine biogeographical province is based mainly on the existence of remote isolated populations in oases all over the desert regions. This notion is now reinforced by the fossil record from Netiv Hagdud, indicating that native populations existed in the Lower Jordan Valley during the Early Neolithic period, where it remains very common.

The collared dove is mainly a graminivorous bird. Nesting sites in the southern Levant are generally on trees but occasionally on ledges. As a highly graminivorous, but no less granivorous form, the initiation of its expansion, first in the Middle East and later on into Europe (before the repeated introductions into these areas as a favored bird by Muslims during the Ottoman Empire), seems to follow the domestication of wheat and barley (Zeist and Bakker-Heeres 1985, 1986). Biologists, ecologists, and zoogeographers in particular, should consider more seriously the great impact of sedentism and early farming on the most recent changes in behavior and distribution of many organisms (Tchernov 1984, 1991a). The attraction of *Streptopelia decaocto* to the area of Netiv Hagdud may have been due to the higher availability of grains around the site. As a higher commensal

species it could have been very successful and highly competitive within the newly created habitats. Indeed the collared dove is quite common in the record of Netiv Hagdud (table 4), and was retrieved from throughout the sequence of the Deep Sounding.

Anseriformes

Anatidae

Representatives of wildfowl constituted a major food source. The 580 skeletal parts that were identified from the site (table 6) suggest the important role that this aquatic and semi-aquatic group of birds played in the economic strategy of the local community.

The stratigraphic distribution of the group through the sequence is distinctly uneven. The highest density—frequency per volume of matrix—was found in the Middle Complex of the Deep Sounding (table 6), and the lowest density was in the Upper Area. The density of duck remains was calculated as number of bones per m^3 of matrix:

1. The Middle Complex has yielded 28.4 specimens per m^3.
2. The Lower Complex has yielded 15.2 specimens per m^3.
3. The Upper Complex has yielded 9.0 specimens per m^3.
4. The Upper Area has yielded only 0.5 specimens per m^3.

Percentage representation of the skeletal elements in the various species of the Anatidae and as a whole, given in table 7 and figures 3 and 4, shows a significant difference in skeletal part representation. Elements connected to the pectoral girdle dominate

AREA	D E E P	S O U N D I N G		UPPER AREA	Total
Element | Complex	Lower complex	Middle Complex	Upper Complex		
Tadorna tadorna					
Coracoid	3(2r+l)(c); 9(5r+4l); 6(4l+2r);	13(7r+6l)(d); 17(9l+8r)(c); 27(15l+12r)(p);	2(r+l)(c); 1(l)(p);	2(r+l)(c);	80
Scapula	5(?)(p); 3(2l+r)(p);	13(?)(p); 20(12l+8r)(p);	1(?)(p); 1(r)(p);	3(?)(p);3(2r+l)(p);	49
Sternum	3(p);	5(p);	-	-	8
Furcula	2(p);	1(p);	-	1(p);	4
Humerus	6(3l+3r)(p);	27(15l+12r)(p); 2(l+r)(d);	-	1(r)(d);	36
Radius	-	2(?)(p);	-	-	2
Ulna	1(r)(c); 2(?)(d);	4(2l+2r)(p); 1(l)(p);	2(?)(d);	1(l)(c);	11
Carpometacarpus	2(l+r)(p); 1(?)(d);	4(2l+2r)(p); 2(r)(d); 1(l)(c);	1(l)(p);	1(l)(p); 1(l)(c);	13
Phalanx 1, wing digit II	-	1(?)(c);	-	-	1
Synsacrum	-	1(i);	-	-	1
Ilium	-	1(r)(p);	-	-	1
Femur	1(r)(p);		-	-	1
Tarsometatarsus	-	1(l)(c);	-	-	1
Quadratum	-	7(?)(c);	-	-	7
Total	**44**	**150**	**8**	**13**	**215**
Anas platyrhynchos					
Coracoid	4(2l+2r)(c); 6(4l+2r); 1(r)(d);	5(3l+2r)(d); 11(6r+5l)(c); 7(4r+3l)(p);	4(2r+2l)(d);2(l)(p);1(l)(c);	-	41
Scapula	2(?)(p); 2(r+l)9P);	8(?)(p); 10(6l+4r)(p);	-	-	22
Sternum	8(p);	18(p);	2(p);	-	28
Furcula	2(p);	13(p);	4(p);	-	19
Humerus	4(l+3r)(p);	6(2l+4r)(p);	2(l)(p);	-	12
Radius	1(?)(p);	1(?)(p);	-	-	2
Carpometacarpus	1(r)(p);	1(r)(p); 1(r)(d);	1(l)(d);	-	2
Femur	1(l)(d);	2(r)(d);	-	-	3
Tibiotarsus	-	1(l)(p);	-	-	2
Total	**32**	**84**	**16**	**0**	**132**
Anas querquedula					
Coracoid	4(1l+3r)(p); 2(l+r)(c); 1(r)(d);	22(11l+11r)(c); 4(2r+2l)(d); 28(15r+13l)(p);	1(r)(c);	-	63
Scapula	3(?)(p); 7(4l+3r)(p);	13(?)(p); 30(15l+15r)(p);	-	-	53
Sternum		5(p);	-	-	5
Furcula	-	8(p);	-	-	8
Humerus	4(2l+2r)(p);	10(5l+5r)(p); 2(r)(d);	1(r)(p);	-	17
Carpometacarpus	-	-	-	1(l)(p);	1
Total	**21**	**122**	**3**	**1**	**147**
Anas albifrons					
Coracoid	-	1(l)(d);	-	-	1
Scapula	-	-	-	1(?)(p);	1
Furcula	1(p);	-	-	-	1
Ulna	1(l)(d);	1(?)(d);	-	-	2
Carpometacarpus	-	2(r)(c); 1(l)(p);	-	-	3
Total	**2**	**5**	**0**	**1**	**8**
Grand Total	**99**	**361**	**27**	**15**	**502**

Table 6

Inventory of Anatidae remains, representation of their skeletal elements, and their distribution along the sequence.
c= complete; i= incomplete; l= left; r= right; p= proximal; d=distal; ?= side unknown.

(coracoid, scapula, sternum, and furcula, and to a lesser extent, humerus and radius). Leg, pelvic girdle, and skull elements are almost completely absent. Except for the quadratum, no other skull elements were found in the assemblage. The only logical explanation for the skewed representation is that skeletal parts which included the pectoral muscles were commonly brought back to the site, while other parts of the carcass and the head were left outside the site perhaps where the birds were hunted. While this discrepancy in skeletal part abundance for all the Anatidae is apparently due to selection on the part of the hunters, we do not have any way to know whether this selection was due to dietary and economic considerations or to other cultural factors. Table 7 displays the amount of meat that could have been

extracted from each of the species and from the Anatidae as a unit. A comparison with other groups is given in the last chapter.

Tadorna tadorna (Linnaeus, 1758)

Palearctic in distribution, during the breeding period the shelduck is largely associated with marine habitats along the coasts and in estuaries. Along its eastern (and main) areas of distribution, breeding habitats are found by inland salt lakes, along rivers, and occasionally in meadows away from open water. Food consists mainly of invertebrates, especially molluscs and crustaceans, collected chiefly by surface digging, dabbling, or scything in exposed mud or shallow water. The shelduck used to be a common transient and wintering bird in the southern Levant. Most of

Skeletal Elements	Anas platyrhynchos	Anas querquedula	Tadorna tadorna	Anser albifrons	Anatidae-Undetermined
Coracoid	41 (31.06%)	63 (42.86%)	80 (37.21%)	1 (12.50%)	34 (43.59%)
Scapula	22 (16.66)%	53 (36.05%)	49 (22.79%)	1 (12.50%)	4 (5.13%)
Sternum	28 (21.21%)	5 (3.40%)	8 (3.72%)	-	23 (29.49%)
Furcula	19 (14.39%)	8 (5.44%)	4 (1.86%)	1 (12.50%)	7 (8.97%)
Humerus	12 (9.09%)	17 (11.56%)	36 (16.74%)	-	2 (2.56%)
Radius	2 (1.51%)	-	2 (0.93%)	-	-
Ulna	-	-	11 (5.11%)	2 (25.00%)	-
Carpometacarpus	2 (1.51%)	1 (0.68%)	13 (6.05%)	3 (37.50%)	1 (1.28%)
Phalanx 1,wing digit II	-	-	1 (0.465%)	-	-
Synsacrum	-	-	1 (0.465%)	-	-
Ilium	-	-	1 (0.465%)	-	-
Femur	2 (1.51%)	-	1 (0.465%)	-	1 (1.28%)
Tibiotarsus	3 (2.27%)	-	-	-	3 (3.85%)
Tarsometatarsus	-	-	1 (0.465%)	-	-
Quadratum	-	-	7 (3.25%)	-	3 (3.85%)
Total	**132**	**147**	**215**	**8**	**78**
					Grand Total: **580**
M.N.I.	**28** (= number of sterni)	**32** (=63/2 corac.+0.5)	**40** (=80/2 corac.)	**2** (=3/2 carpomet.+0.5)	**23** (=number of sterni) Grand Total: **125**
Total Weight Estimation (kg)*	28x950= **26.600**	32x425=**13.600**	40x1165=**46.600**	2x220=**4.400**	23x846.6= **19.472** Grand Total: **91.2**

Table 7

Number of skeletal elements and their percentage representation in the family Anatidae, and the minimum number of individuals (MNI) per skeletal part. Assuming that each hunted individual reflects a complete carcass consumed in the site, the meat weight estimation (following Smith 1972) is also represented.

*Weight of *Anas platyrhynchos*: 900–1000 gr (mean=950).
*Weight of *Anas querquedula*: 350–500 gr (mean=425).
*Weight of *Tadorna tadorna*: 830–1500 gr (mean=1165).
*Weight of *Anser albifrons*: 1800–2600 gr (mean=2200).

the Levantine populations originated from eastern Europe and northern Asia.

Tadorna tadorna is the most abundant water bird in the assemblage; 215 bones were recovered, belonging to 40 individuals (using standard MNI procedure), and the estimated amount of meat was 46 kg (tables 6, 7). This species was described by Pichon (1984) from the Natufian layers of Eynan (Mallaha; Upper Jordan Valley), and Hayonim Cave (western Galilee). Bone measurements of the Neolithic population from Netiv Hagdud are presented in table 8, in comparison with Natufian representatives from Eynan and Hayonim. The number of specimens is too small, however, to show changes in size or proportions of elements during the interval between the two periods.

Tadorna tadorna was found in the Lower Pleistocene deposits of the 'Ubeidiya Formation (Tchernov 1980), showing the great antiquity of the species in the region and the consistency of its migration routes.

Anas platyrhynchos Linnaeus, 1758

Holarctic, the mallard is adapted to an extremely wide range of habitats, from arctic tundra to subtropical zones. The species occupies essentially still and

shallow waters, ranging from fresh and brackish to estuaries, lagoons, or coastal saline waters. It prefers ample plant growth, sometimes dense stands of reeds. At present, all kinds of artificial water bodies are attractive to this species, and consequently it exhibits a high tolerance to human presence and can easily exploit highly disturbed anthropogenic sites. A wide range of food types and feeding habits that change with seasons and habitats characterizes this genetically diversified species and allows it to use a wide range of habitats.

While predominantly migratory, in the southern Levant most populations are passing transients and wintering birds. Recent recoveries of legbands indicate that the great majority of the southern Levantine populations originate in eastern Europe and northern Asia (Yom-Tov 1988). A few populations of mallards were recorded as summer breeders and some even as residents in this region. As for the representatives of this species in Netiv Hagdud, it is difficult to conclude what their status was. The relatively large number of specimens recovered from the site may indicate that they were chiefly hunted during the migratory seasons, when they would have been found in large

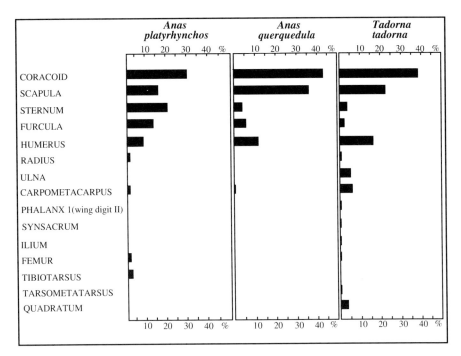

Figure 3
Relative representation of skeletal parts of several species of Anatidae in the PPNA of Netiv Hagdud. There is a clear preference for the "triosseum" skeletal complex (scapula, coracoid, and sternum), probably indicating a special preference for the pectoral muscles.

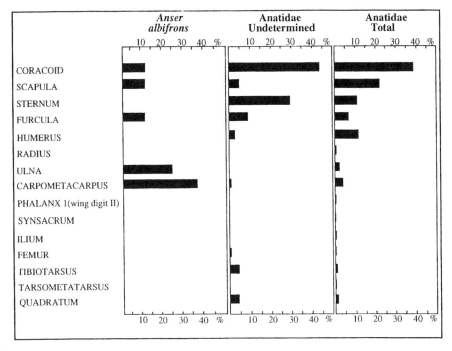

Figure 4
Relative representation of skeletal parts of several species of Anatidae and the genus *Anser*. There is a clear preference for the "triosseum" skeletal complex (scapula, coracoid, and sternum) also shown by the goose, probably indicating a special preference for the pectoral muscles.

sons, when they would have been found in large flocks.

The second most abundant species of water bird in the assemblage, 132 mallard bones were identified from the site, mainly from the Middle Complex but none from the Upper Area (table 6). Absolute numbers and percentages of bone representation are given in tables 6 and 7 and figure 3. The estimated amount of meat obtained from this species is 26.6 kg. A comparison with other species of anatids is given in table 7, and measurements of the skeletal elements compared with the Natufian population from Eynan (Huleh valley) as described by Pichon (1984) is given in table 9. No significant differences in skeletal sizes are found between the two populations.

Anas querquedula Linnaeus, 1758

Basically a trans-Palearctic species, found usually north of 40°, the garganey breeds mainly within Mediterranean, steppe, and temperate climatic zones and is found occasionally in the boreal region. It favors narrow or well-compartmented sheltered and shallow standing fresh water surrounded by grassland or a variety of wetland habitats and with luxurious floating and emergent vegetation. Normally a daytime feeder in pairs, small, or large flocks, it feeds chiefly on plant and animal materials collected while swimming with head submerged, occasionally collecting items above the water surface.

The garganey is distinguished from other members of its genus, most of which winter all across northern tropics, by being fully migratory. Mainly transient in the southern Levant, it is found in large numbers during the migratory periods on the way to and from Africa.

Some 122 bones were collected predominantly from the Middle Complex (table 6). As a small-size duck, the estimated amount of meat yielded was 13.6 kg (table 7). Measurements of some of the skeletal parts are given in table 10 and compared with some of the individuals that were described by Pichon (1984) from the Natufian layers of Mureybet (Syria) and Eynan (Mallaha) (Huleh Valley). No significant size differences are found between the Neolithic and the Natufian representatives of this species.

Anser albifrons (Scopoli, 1769)

Essentially boreal in distribution, the white-fronted goose is located mainly in eastern Europe and northern Asia, in shrubby tundra close to rivers, lakes, and pools. A vegetarian, it feeds chiefly on leaves, stems, stolons, rhizoms, tubers, and seeds by grazing and pecking. At present, it is occasionally found as a transient bird in the southern Levant during the migratory seasons.

Tadorna tadorna	N	E	T	I	V	H	A	G	D	U	D	HAYONIM CAVE		EYNAN (MALLAHA)	
	Min.	Max.	x	∂	Var.	v	Std.Error	n	95% Lower	95% Upper		Mean	n	Mean	n
Elements															
Carpometacarpus															
Total Length	52.81	59.19	57.130	2.995	8.968	5.242	1.497	4	52.365	61.895		-	-	-	-
Width of Distal End	7.70	8.98	8.420	0.611	0.373	7.252	0.305	4	7.448	9.392		-	-	-	-
Width of Proximal End	12.46	14.98	13.833	0.904	0.817	6.634	0.369	6	12.885	14.782		-	-	13.6	1
Diameter of Trochlea Carpalis	5.43	6.57	6.026	0.388	0.151	6.441	0.151	8	5.702	6.351		-	-	6.4	-
Humerus															
Width of Proximal End	20.02	22.78	21.428	0.868	0.753	4.049	0.204	18	20.997	21.860		-	-	-	-
Width of Distal End	12.73	14.44	13.720	0.822	0.675	5.988	0.411	4	12.413	15.027		13.65	2	14.475	4
Coracoid															
Greatest Length	49.38	57.84	53.108	2.804	7.863	5.280	0.845	11	51.224	54.992		-	-	-	-
Lesser Length	44.97	53.33	48.831	3.046	9.279	6.238	0.963	10	46.652	51.010		-	-	-	-
Tip of Proc. Procoracoideum to Prox. End of Acrocoracoideum	11.8	15.95	13.878	1.119	1.252	8.064	0.187	36	13.57	14.257		-	-	-	-
Scapula															
Width of Proximal End	11.02	13.81	12.289	0.770	0.593	6.266	0.110	49	12.067	12.51		-	-	10.8	3
Tibiotarsus															
Total Length	-	-	93.39	-	-	-	-	1	-	-		-	-	-	-
Width of Distal End	-	-	10.23	-	-	-	-	1	-	-		-	-	-	-
Tarsometatarsus															
Total Length	-	-	51.95	-	-	-	-	1	-	-		-	-	-	-
Width of Distal End	-	-	11.32	-	-	-	-	1	-	-		-	-	10.0	2
Width of Proximal End	-	-	11.15	-	-	-	-	1	-	-		-	-	-	-

Table 8

Measurements (in mm) of several skeletal elements remains of Anatidae compared with Natufian populations (Pichon 1984).

n = number of specimens studied, x = mean, ∂ = Standard deviation, v = coefficient of variation, min = minimum value observed, max = maximum value observed, 95% lower = 95% confidence interval of the mean, 95% upper = 95% confidence interval of the mean.

Anas platyrhynchos	N E T I V		H A G D U D								HAYONIM CAVE		EYNAN (MALLAHA)	
	Min.	Max.	x	∂	Var.	v	Std.Error	n	95% Lower	95% Upper	Mean	n	Mean	n
Elements														
Humerus														
Total Length	-	-	97.12	-	-	-	-	1	-	-	92.1	1	-	-
Width of Proximal End	17.68	19.15	18.278	0.768	0.590	4.199	0.443	3	16.379	20.194	19.8	1	20.97	9
Width of Distal End	-	-	-	-	-	-	-	-	-	-	-	-	-	-
Coracoid														
Greatest Length	42.000	48.888	45.163	3.473	12.063	7.690	2.005	3	36.353	53.791	-	-	53.70	1
Lesser Length	37.120	44.97	42.586	2.671	7.134	6.272	0.944	8	40.353	44.820	-	-	-	-
Tip of Proc. Procoracoideum to Prox. End of Acrocoracoideum	11.48	15.35	12.835	0.895	0.801	6.975	0.217	17	12.374	13.295	-	-	-	-
Scapula														
Width of Proximal End	9.170	11.310	10.382	0.596	0.355	5.736	0.144	17	10.076	10.689	10.35	2	11.00	3

Table 9
Measurements (in mm) of several skeletal elements remains of Anatidae compared with Natufian populations (Pichon 1984). n = number of specimens studied, x = mean, ∂ = Standard deviation, v = coefficient of variation, min = minimum value observed, max = maximum value observed, 95% lower = 95% confidence interval of the mean, 95% upper = 95% confidence interval of the mean.

Only 8 isolated bones were found, 5 of which come from the Middle Complex (table 6). From the two calculated MNI, 4.4 kg of meat could have been used (table 7).

It is worth noting that *Anser albifrons* was also found in the Lower Pleistocene deposits of the 'Ubeidiya Formation (Jordan Valley), showing the great antiquity of the migration route of this species (Tchernov 1980). Pichon (1984) described a few specimens of this species of goose from the Natufian layers of Hayonim Cave (western Galilee), but mentioned other species of *Anser* (*A. erythropus* from the Natufian of Eynan and *A. anser* from the Natufian of Eynan, Hayonim, and Mureybet).

Undetermined Anatidae

The inventory of undetermined Anatidae bones is given in table 11. These 78 specimens were generally too fragmentary to permit more detailed identification, but most if not all of them probably came from one of the three most common representatives of the Anatini (*Tadorna* and *Anas*). Comparison with the other anatids is given in table 7 and figure 4. The amount of meat that the 23 MNI could have supplied is estimated at 19.4 kg. The total meat weight that the whole group could have supplied is estimated to be 110.6 kg.

Accipitriformes and Falconiformes

The southern Levant plays a crucial role in the Eurasian-African bird migration. In particular, the

Anas querquedula	N E T I V		H A G D U D								MUREYBET		EYNAN (MALLAHA)	
	Min.	Max.	x	∂	Var.	v	Std.Error	n	95% Lower	95% Upper	Mean	n	Mean	n
Elements														
Carpometacarpus														
Total Length	-	-	-	-	-	-	-	-	-	-	-	-	-	-
Width of Distal End	-	-	-	-	-	-	-	-	-	-	-	-	-	-
Width of Proximal End	-	-	8.410	-	-	-	-	1	-	-	9.07	13	-	-
Diameter of Trochlea Carpalis	-	-	4.070	-	-	-	-	1	-	-	4.08	13	-	-
Humerus														
Total Length	-	-	8.890	-	-	-	-	1	-	-	-	-	-	-
Width of Proximal End	12.46	14.06	13.323	0.537	0.288	4.031	0.155	12	12.982	12.665	13.30	3	-	-
Width of Distal End	-	-	-	-	-	-	-	-	-	-	-	-	-	-
Coracoid														
Greatest Length	34.00	35.49	34.637	0.523	0.274	1.511	0.198	7	34.153	35.121	-	-	-	-
Lesser Length	31.55	32.85	32.119	0.513	0.263	1.596	0.194	7	31.644	32.593	-	-	-	-
Tip of Proc. Procoracoideum to Prox. End of Acrocoracoideum	7.95	10.07	8.950	0.495	0.245	5.531	0.084	35	8.780	9.120	-	-	-	-
Scapula														
Width of Proximal End	6.97	8.65	7.839	0.414	0.171	5.281	0.0580	51	7.722	7.955	7.98	5	7.51	5

Table 10
Measurements (in mm) of several skeletal elements remains of Anatidae compared with Natufian populations (Pichon 1984). n = number of specimens studied, x = mean, ∂ = Standard deviation, v = coefficient of variation, min = minimum value observed, max = maximum value observed, 95% lower = 95% confidence interval of the mean, 95% upper = 95% confidence interval of the mean.

Jordan Rift Valley, the Gulf of Aqaba, and the Red Sea funnel many species of birds during the migratory period. Bird migration in the southern Levantine region has always been a pronounced phenomenon. The unique biogeographical position of the area, encompassing the eastern Mediterranean coast and the Syro-African Rift Valley, makes the Levant one of the major migration routes from Palearctica to Africa. A large component of the migratory birds lands and rests in this area before (spring) and after (autumn) crossing the Saharo-Arabian deserts. Medium- and large-size birds, mainly of eastern European origin, encircle the Mediterranean Sea during the migration period and pass along the eastern Mediterranean shores (Yom-Tov 1988). Similarly, the Red Sea funnels medium- to large-size birds through the desert region of southwest Asia. As a result, 130 Palearctic species are presently regular migrants, of which over 100 species winter in the southern Levant; about 140 species have been recorded as vagrants, and 170 species of birds are year-round residents or occasional breeders.

Among the migrants, the accipitriformes and fal-coniformes play a significant role. During the migration period, millions of raptors are seen along the coastal and Jordan Valley routes, many of which come down to rest, to roost, or to prey. For example, 200,000 *Pernis apivorus*, (a species identified from Netiv Hagdud), passed over the Gulf of Elat during two days in May 1984, and 320,000 passed over the coastal region during two days in September 1984 (Yom-Tov 1988). Usually, the migration of some 80 percent of the individuals of a raptor species takes place in a relatively short period, sometimes limited to only a few days. Thus during the migration period there are many opportunities to watch and hunt roosting individuals all along their migratory routes. Netiv Hagdud is situated precisely along the main migratory route of the Jordan Valley, where, before crossing the Dead Sea area, many birds may rest for the night, or sometimes even for a few days. It seems that the inhabitants of Netiv Hagdud took advantage of this phenomenon and hunted quite a few falconi-formes, favoring mainly one species (see below).

The stratigraphic distribution of the skeletal remains through the sequence was found to be uneven. Much as with the Anatidae, the highest frequency per volume of matrix (density) was found in the Middle Complex of the Deep Sounding, and the lowest in the Upper Area as follows:

1. The Middle Complex has yielded 9.37 items per m³ of matrix.
2. The Lower Complex has yielded 2.92 items per m³ of matrix
3. The Upper Complex has yielded 1.33 items per m³ of matrix.
4. The Upper Area has yielded 0.064 items per m³ of matrix.

An inventory of the raptor remains and the percentage representation of skeletal elements for the various species is given in tables 12 and 13. In general (compared with skeletal representation in the Anatidae, table 6; figs. 3, 4), the skeletal part distribution is much less skewed. However, what skewing there is appears as the reverse of the anatids: in general, foot elements are more abundant than elements from the pectoral girdle and the forelimbs. Obviously the local inhabitants handled most of the falconi-

AREA	D E E P	S O U N D I N G		UPPER AREA	Total
Element | Complex	Lower complex	Middle Complex	Upper Complex		
Anatidae-Undetermined					
Coracoid	3(2l+1r)(d);	22(10l+12r)(p); 3(l+2r)(d); 4(2r+2l)(c);	-	2(r+l)(p);	34
Scapula	-	3(?)(p);	1(?)(p);	-	4
Sternum	4(p);	19(p);	-	-	23
Furcula	-	7(p);	-	-	7
Humerus	-	2(r+l)(p);	-	-	2
Carpometacarpus	1(r)(d);	-	-	-	1
Femur	1(l)(p);	-	-	-	1
Tibiotarsus	-	2(r+l)(d); 1(l)(p);	-	-	3
Quadratum	-	2(?)(c);	1(?)(c);	-	3
Total	**9**	**65**	**2**	**2**	**78**

Table 11

Inventory of undetermined remains of Anatidae; representation of their skeletal elements, and their distribution along the sequence.

c= complete; i= incomplete; l= left; r= right; p= proximal; d=distal; /= side unknown.

formes (except probably *Milvus migrans*, see below) differently from ducks. The body part frequencies indicate that very often, and in contrast with the ducks, they did bring the whole body (except the skull) to the site area. Additionally, most of the species they selected had femora, tibiotarsi, tarsometatarsi, and many phalanxes that could be used as tools. Claws, for instance, may have been used for harpoons. There is no evidence at Netiv Hagdud that claws were used for fishing, however, so they could have served different functions (Solecki and McGovern 1980; Solecki and Solecki 1983). The impression gained is that raptors were used for many different purposes and not only as food resources. Table 13 shows the amount of meat that could have been obtained from each one of the species and from the group as a whole.

Accipitridae

Milvus migrans (Boddaert, 1783)

Predominantly Paleotropic and Palearctic where it occupies Mediterranean and low-latitude steppe zones, the black kite is also found in temperate to boreal regions. Most of the Palearctic populations are migratory, but southern European populations are largely resident. As a predator and a scavenger it displays a wide dietary spectrum that mainly reflects an opportunistic approach to seasonality and food availability.

This species used to be a common breeder in the Mediterranean belt of the Levant. Its main migratory routes along the Mediterranean were recorded through Suez, crossing the Negev and Sinai deserts (Bijlisma 1982). The other major route goes mainly along the Syro-African Rift Valley (Christensen et al. 1981).

The black kite is the predominant raptor of Netiv Hagdud of which 71 specimens were identified. While at present *Pernis apivorus* is conspicuously more common during the Jordan Rift Valley migration (a situation that might have been constant over time) the frequency of kites in Netiv Hagdud is twice as great as all other identified raptors (table 13). It is also possible that some populations of *Milvus migrans* were resident in the Lower Jordan area and thus accessible for hunters throughout the year. The amount of meat that could have been recovered from this species alone is estimated to be 12.6 kg (table 13).

Worth noting is the complete absence of coracoids and sterni of all the raptors except for *Milvus migrans*, and the unidentified falconiformes (figs. 5, 6), the majority of which may be *Milvus migrans* as well. It is thus assumed that in contrast with all other raptors, kites were butchered in a similar manner as were ducks, namely by tearing the pectoral muscles out of the carcass. All of the other raptors were probably used for other purposes (see distribution of skeletal parts in figs. 5, 6).

Pernis apivorus (Linnaeus, 1758)

Distribution of the honey buzzard chiefly covers the middle and upper latitudes of the western Palearctic. In its breeding and wintering ranges, it is not usually gregarious but does form large flocks during the migration period (Christensen et al. 1981; Bijlisma 1982). Yom-Tov (1988) has pointed out that 320,000 individuals passed along the Jordan Rift Valley and the Gulf of Elat in two days (September 10–11, 1982). Most of the populations winter mainly in the wooded country of equatorial Africa.

During the peak of the migration period the availability of weak and ill specimens could be rather large. Thus, the chances are that the six specimens that have been recovered from the Lower and Middle Complex (tables 12, 13), could have been taken in the field without using special hunting devices.

Buteo rufinus (Cretzschmar, 1827)

A southern Palearctic bird, the long-legged buzzard used to be a common breeder in lowland arid and semiarid steppes of the Southern Levant. It feeds chiefly on small mammals, reptiles, and large insects and requires access to water. The populations of higher latitudes are migratory but essentially resident in the southern fringes of the arid Palearctic belt.

Four bones were recovered from the Middle Complex. The bones may either represent migratory individuals, residents, or both.

Buteo buteo (Linnaeus, 1758)

A trans-Palearctic polytypic species, chiefly distributed in the temperate and boreal latitudes in varied landscapes, this buzzard feeds on a wide spectrum of prey ranging from small mammals to large insects. It is a very common transient and wintering bird in the southern Levant, mainly originating in the eastern Palearctic. Around a half-million migrating buzzards were recorded yearly during the springs of 1981, 1982, and 1987 (Christensen et al. 1981). The fossil record is confined to three items (table 12).

AREA	D E E P S O U N D I N G			UPPER AREA	Total
Element | Complex	Lower complex	Middle Complex	Upper Complex		
Milvus migrans					
Coracoid	1(r)(c); 1(l)(d); 1(r)(p);	2(r+l)(d); 4 (3r+l)(p); 4(2r+2l)(c);	1(r)c);	-	14
Sternum	-	3(p);	-	-	3
Humerus	1(r)(d);	3(r+2l)(p); 3(2r+l)(d);	-	-	7
Radius	-	1(r)(p);	-	-	1
Ulna	-	2(r)(c); 1(l)(d); 1(l)(p);	-	-	4
Carpometacarpus	-	1(l)(c); 6(3l+3r)(p); 1(l)(d);	-	-	8
Phalanx 1, wing digit II	-	11 (?)(c);	-	-	11
Synsacrum	-	1(i);	-	-	1
Femur	-	1(l)(c); 3(l+2r)(p);	-	1(l)(c);	5
Tibiotarsus	3(l+2r)(d);	4(2l+2r)(d);	-	-	7
Tarsometatarsus	2(r)(p);	2(l+r)(p); 3(l+2r)(d);	-	1(l)(d);	8
Phalanx 1 (foot)	-	2(?)(c);	-	-	2
Total	**9**	**59**	**1**	**2**	**71**
Pernis apivorus					
Humerus	2(l+r)(p);	-	-	-	2
Carpometacarpus	-	1(r)(p);	-	-	1
Femur	-	1(r)(p);	-	-	1
Tibiotarsus	-	1(l)(d);	-	-	1
Tarsometatarsus	-	1(l)(p);	-	-	1
Total	**2**	**4**	**0**	**0**	**6**
Buteo rufinus					
Ulna	-	1(r)(d);	-	-	1
Carpometacarpus	-	1(l)(p);	-	-	1
Phalanx 1, wing digit II	-	1(?)(c);	-	-	1
Tarsometatarsus	-	1(l)(d);	-	-	1
Total	**0**	**4**	**0**	**0**	**4**
Buteo buteo					
Carpometacarpus	-	-	-	1(l)(d);	1
Phalanx 1, wing digit II	-	1(?)(c);	-	-	1
Tibiotarsus	-	1(r)(d);	-	-	1
Total	**0**	**2**	**0**	**1**	**3**
Aquila pomarina					
Carpometacarpus	1(r)(p);	-	1(l)(d);	-	2
Phalanx 1, wing digit II	-	1(?)(c);	-	-	1
Tibiotarsus	-	1(l)(d);	-	-	1
Total	**1**	**2**	**1**	**0**	**4**
Aquila sp.					
Ulna	1(l)(p);	-	-	-	1
Tarsometatarsus	-	1(r)(d);	1(l)(p);	-	2
Phalanx 1 (foot)	-	1(?)(c);	-	1(?)(c);	2
Phalanx last (foot)	-	1(?)(c);	-		1
Total	**1**	**3**	**1**	**1**	**6**
Falco spp.					
Coracoid	-	3(r+2l)(p);	-	-	3
Carpometacarpus	-	1(r)(p);	-	-	1
Phalanx 1, wing digit II	-	1(?)(c);	-	1(?)(c);	2
Femur	-	1(l)(c);	-	-	1
Total	**0**	**6**	**0**	**1**	**7**
Circus sp.					
Humerus	-	-	1(l)(p);	-	1
Tibiotarsus	-	1(r)(d);	-	-	1
Total	**0**	**1**	**1**	**0**	**2**
Accipiter sp.					
Humerus	-	1(r)(p);	-	-	1
Tibiotarsus	-	2(l)(d);	-	-	2
Tarsometatarsus	-	1(l)(p);	-	-	1
Total	**0**	**4**	**0**	**0**	**4**
Falconiformes Undeter.					
Coracoid	1(l)(d); 1(?)(i);	-	-	-	2
Sternum	1(p);	2(p);	-	-	3
Humerus	-	2(l+r)(p);	-	-	2
Ulna	1(r)(d);	-	-	-	1
Carpometacarpus	-	3(l+2r)(d);	-	-	3
Tarsometatarsus	1(l)(p);	2(l+r)(p); 2(r+l)(d);	-	-	5
Phalanx 1 (foot)	1(?)(c);	17(?)(c);	-	3(?)(c);	21
Phalanx last (foot)	-	6(?)(c);	-	-	6
Total	**6**	**34**	**0**	**3**	**43**
Grand Total	**19**	**119**	**4**	**8**	**150**

Table 12

Inventory of Falconiformes remains, representation of their skeletal elements, and their distribution along the sequence.

c= complete; i= incomplete; l= left; r= right; p= proximal; d=distal; /= side unknown.

Skeletal Elements	Milvus migrans	Buteo + Pernis	Aquila spp.	Falco+Circus +Accipiter	Falconiformes Undetermined	Falconiformes Total
Coracoid	14 (19.72%)	-	-	-	2 (4.65%)	19 (12.66%)
Sternum	3 (4.22%)	-	-	-	3 (6.97%)	6 (4.00%)
Furcula	-	-	-	-	-	3 (4.22%)
Humerus	7 (9.86%)	2 (15.38%)	-	2 (15.38%)	2 (4.65%)	13 (8.66%)
Radius	1 (1.41%)	-	-	-	-	1 (0.66%)
Ulna	4 (5.63%)	1 (7.69%)	1 (10%)	-	1 (2.32%)	7 (4.66%)
Carpometacarpus	8 (11.27%)	3 (23.70%)	2 (20%)	1 (7.69%)	3 (6.97%)	17 (11.33%)
Phalanx 1, wing digit II	11 (15.49%)	2 (15.38%)	1 (10%)	2 (15.38%)	-	16 (10.66%)
Synsacrum	1 (1.41%)	-	-	-	-	1 (0.66%)
Femur	5 (7.04%)	1 (7.69%)	-	1 (7.69%)	-	7 (4.66%)
Tibiotarsus	7 (9.86%)	2 (15.38%)	1 (10%)	3 (23.70%)	-	13 (8.66%)
Tarsometatarsus	8 (11.27%)	2 (15.38%)	2 (20%)	1 (7.69%)	5 (11.63%)	18 (12.00%)
Phalanx 1 (foot)	2 (2.82%)	-	2 (20%)	-	21 (48.84%)	25 (16.66%)
Phalanx 3 (foot)	-	-	1 (10%)	-	6 (13.95%)	7 (4.66%)
Total	**71**	**13**	**10**	**13**	**43**	**Grand Total: 150**
M.N.I.	**7**(=14/2 corac.)	**3** (=3 species)	**2** (=2 species)	**4** (=4 different species)	**6** (=21/4 phal. +0.5)	**9** (=19/2 corac. +0.5)
Total Weight Estimation (kg)*	7x900= **6.3**	3x900= **2.7**	2x1400= **2.8**	4x300= **1.2**	Mean weight=1,000gr 6x1000= **6.0**	Mean weigth=900gr 29x900= 21,100 **Grand Total: 19.8**

Table 13
Number of skeletal elements and their percentage representation in the family Accipitridae and the minimum number of individuals (MNI) . Assuming that each hunted individual reflects a complete carcass consumed in the site, the meat/weight estimation is also represented. Weights of the falconiform birds were taken from Cramp and Simmons 1980.
*Weight of *Milvus migrans*: 600-1200 gr (x=900).
*Weight of *Buteo + Pernis*: 500–800 gr ; 600–1300 gr (x=425).
*Weight of *Aquila* : 1200–1600 gr (x=1400).
*Weight of *Falco + Circus + Accipiter*: 120–1000 gr (x=300).

Aquila pomarina C. L. Brehm, 1831
A west-central Palearctic and Himalayan bird, the lesser spotted eagle winters almost entirely in tropical Africa. It feeds principally on small mammals and other vertebrates. This eagle is a very common migrant along the migratory routes of the southern Levant (Yom-Tov 1988). Four specimens were recovered from different layers of Netiv Hagdud (tables 12, 13).

Aquila spp.
Probably more than one species is represented by the six bones that were retrieved from all the different complexes (table 12). At least some of the remains can be attributed to either *Aquila pomarina* or *Aquila clanga*. The material is too fragmentary for further identification.

Circus sp.
This genus is represented by only two bone fragments (table 12) that fall within the size range of *Circus aeruginosus*. This species was known as a regular breeder in the area, but most of the populations of this and other species are passage migrants.

Accipiter sp.
The fossil record is confined to four bones (table 12). Representatives of this genus are chiefly transient or wintering birds in the southern Levant. At present *Accipiter brevipes* is the most common migrant of this genus along the Jordan Rift Valley.

Falconidae
Falco spp.
At least two different classes are represented by the seven bones (table 12). One is comparable in size to *Falco tinnunculus*, and the other group belongs to a very large species that matches the size of *Falco cherrug*. Some of the species may have been residents in the area of Netiv Hagdud, like *Falco naumanni* or *Falco concolor*.

Forty-three bones (table 12) were indeterminate due to their fragmentary preservation. Many of them seem to belong to above mentioned species, mainly *Milvus migrans*.

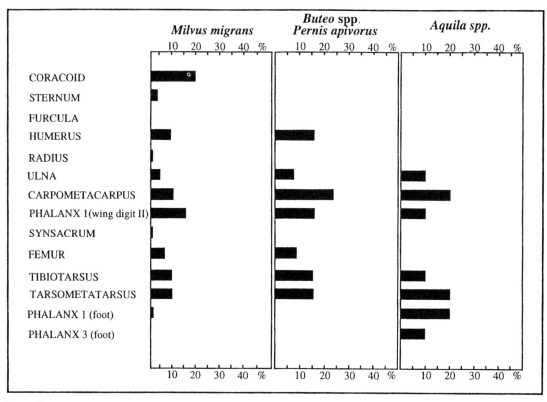

Figure 5
Relative representation of skeletal parts of several species of Falconiformes. During these periods there is a clear preference for collecting foot phalanxes, as well as tarsometatarsi and tibiotarsi.

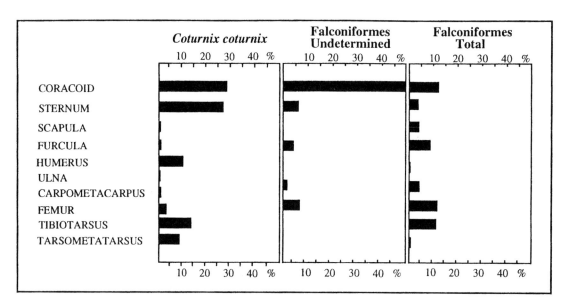

Figure 6
Relative representation of skeletal parts of all the undetermined Falconiformes, and the Falconiformes as a group in comparison with *Coturnix coturnix* (quail).

Galliformes

Phasianidae

Alectoris chukar (J. E. Gray, 1830)

The chukar partridge is a very common Palearctic genus of partridge and constituted one of the main food resources in the Natufian period. Therefore, it seems important to present this species in some detail. Of the seven known species of partridge, only *Alectoris chukar* is widely distributed over Asia and the Mediterranean region, exploiting as it does a wide variety of ecological situations. *Alectoris chukar* displays sympatry with most of the Old World partridges. Two subspecies have been attributed to this species in the southern Levant: *Alectoris chukar cypriotes* whose range roughly covers the Mediterranean climatic belt, and *Alectoris chukar sinaica* which is widely distributed over the arid zone of the Levant. Conclusive differences between the two subspecies are still a matter of dispute, but the southern Sinai populations seem to represent glacial relicts (Tchernov 1982) that indeed have accumulated some morphological differences. All the rest of the southern Levantine populations apparently belong to a large undisturbed deme.

The habitats of the chukar partridge range from typical Mediterranean climates to extreme arid zones, and from lowland plains up to 3000 m altitude. Ready access to water is sometimes noted as obligatory. There is some preference among the Levantine populations to occupy mainly rough ground and rocky hill country. These populations are extremely sedentary; philopatry is characteristic of the group. This behavioral pattern could explain the slow recovery of populations after over exploitation or massive hunting during the past, including during the Natufian period (Pichon 1984, 1987, 1989; Bar-Yosef and Tchernov 1966). In all late Epipaleolithic sites *Alectoris chukar* is the most common bird hunted, predominant over all other avian species. Indeed the relative rarity of this species in the site of Netiv Hagdud may be the result of a late Natufian over-hunting process (tables 14, 15).

The identified skeletal elements are given in tables 14 and 15 and in figure 7. The sparse occurrence of this important species in the fossil record of Netiv Hagdud may be due to its rarity in the area rather than to any specific anthropological behavior. Measurements are given in table 16.

Francolinus francolinus (Linnaeus, 1766)

Formerly a probable circum-Mediterranean species, the black francolin is now restricted to the southeastern Palearctic, from the Near East to Nepal, usually in warmer and somewhat humid climatic areas. This shy and extremely terrestrial gamebird is obligatorily associated with dense vegetation near marshes, rivers, lakes, and other permanent water bodies, feeding mainly on wide variety of plants and animals, but especially seeds and insects collected on the ground. The retrieval of francolins in the Netiv Hagdud assemblage supports the idea that not only were freshwater bodies in abundance in the vicinity of the site, but that the landscape was rich with thick vegetation cover as well.

Sixteen skeletal remains were identified, mainly from the Middle Complex (tables 14, 15), of which 10 are coracoids (fig. 7). The predominance of coracoids may indicate a strict preference for the pectoral muscles, leading to the puzzling question of why the furcula and scapula are absent from the record. The two tarsometatarsi show them to be males. Measurements are given in table 16.

Ammoperdix heyi (Temminck, 1825)

Mainly a circum-Arabian and Sudanese desert and semi-desert species, within its distributional range the sand partridge also occupies more humid enclaves, especially large oases where sparse vegetation and some accessible water are available. Omnivorous and highly adapted for climbing steep-sided banks, the species is resident throughout its range.

Today, the sand partridge is found along the Jordan Rift Valley as far north as the Golan Heights (Yom-Tov, 1988). Remains of *Ammoperdix* were found in the Middle Pleistocene deposits of Oumm Qatafa Cave in the Judean Desert (Tchernov 1962), indicating the great antiquity of the species in the Dead Sea area.

The record from Netiv Hagdud is confined to four items, three of which were recovered from the Lower Complex (tables 14 and 15).

Coturnix coturnix (Linnaeus, 1758)

In many ways this polytypic, wide-range Palearctic and African species remains enigmatic; the actual nature of its distribution and migration routes is very complex. As Palearctic quail populations have suffered marked fluctuations in numbers due to massive hunting during the last two centuries, it is difficult to deduce from the present situation its past migrational

AREA	D E E P S O U N D I N G			UPPER AREA	Total
Element | Complex	Lower complex	Middle Complex	Upper Complex		
Coturnix coturnix					
Coracoid	2(l+r)(d); 1(l)(c);	8(3r+5l)(c); 15(8l+6r)(d); 5(2r+3l)(p);	2(2l)(d); 1(r)(c); 1(r)(p);	-	35
Sternum	2(p);	28(p);	2(p);	2(p);	34
Scapula	-	1(r)(p);	-	-	1
Furcula	-	2(p);	-	-	2
Humerus	1(r)(p);	4(2r+2l)(d); 5(2r+3l)(p);	-	1(l)(d);	11
Ulna	-	-	1(l)(d);	-	1
Carpometacarpus	-	2(r+l)(p);	-	-	2
Femur	-	1(l)(d); 3(l+2r)(p);	1(r)(p);	-	5
Tibiotarsus	1(r)(d);	1(l)(c); 15(7l+8r)(d);	1(l)(d);	-	18
Tarsometatarsus	1(r)(d);	2(l)(c); 3(3l+r)(d); 3(2r+l)(p);	1(l)(d);	2(r+l)(d);	12
Total	**7**	**98**	**10**	**5**	**121**
Francolinus francolinus					
Coracoid	1(l)(d);	4(l+3r)(c); 3(2r+l)(p);	1(l)(d);	1(r)(c);	10
Sternum	-	1(p);	-	-	1
Ulna	-	1(l)(p);	-	-	1
Carpometacarpus	-	1**(r)(d);**	-	-	1
Femur	-	1(r)(d);	-	-	1
Tarsometatarsus	-	*2 (l)(p);	-	-	2
Total	**1**	**13**	**1**	**1**	**16**
Alectoris chukar					
Furcula	1(p);	-	-	-	1
Tibiotarsus	-	1(r)(d);	-	-	1
Tarsometatarsus	-	1(l)(d);	-	-	1
Total	**1**	**2**	**0**	**0**	**3**
Ammoperdix heyi					
Coracoid	1(l)(d);	1(l)(d);	-	-	2
Humerus	1(r)(p);	-	-	-	1
Tarsometatarsus	1(l)(d);	-	-	-	1
Total	**3**	**1**	**0**	**0**	**4**
Grand Total	**12**	**115**	**11**	**6**	**144**

Table 14
Inventory of Phasianidae remains, representation of their skeletal elements, and their distribution along the sequence.
c=complete; i=incomplete; l=left; r=right;p=proximal;d=distal;?=side unknown;*=male.

and distributional behavior. This fact is of importance as the conspicuous decline of the eastern Palearctic populations could have eliminated some of the migratory routes that were used in the past, including the route that goes along the Syro-African Rift Valley. Most of the Palearctic populations are predominantly migratory and generally winter in the drier zone of the Ethiopian realm. While at present most of the migrants cross the Mediterranean on their way to Africa, the Syro-African Rift Valley route is not heavily used. Autumn passage across the Mediterranean takes place mainly from late August to October, and the departure of most of the migratory populations from their winter quarters in the spring is from March to mid-May (peaking in April) (Zuckerbrott et al. 1980; Cramp and Simmons 1980; Yom-Tov 1988). It is thus assumed that the main movement along the Rift Valley took place roughly during the same periods in the Neolithic. Quail could have been hunted in September or May or in both seasons.

As for habitat preferences, quail usually occupy wide-open spaces, both in their winter quarters and their summer breeding areas. It seems that the Netiv Hagdud landscape could not have been used for the long term but only for short rests during broken migratory flight in April and/or September. Quail were also found in the PPNB site of Wadi Tbeik in southern Sinai (Tchernov and Bar-Yosef 1982), indicating that this route, which is rarely used at present, was in use during that period and was exploited by the people who happened to live along it.

The phasianids are represented primarily by 121 *Coturnix coturnix* bones recovered from all the excavated areas, but mainly from the Middle Complex (table 14). Percentage representation of the skeletal elements is given in table 15, and compared with the other genera of phasianids (fig. 7). The relative abundance of the skeletal elements, especially of quail, is significantly skewed (table 15, fig. 7) toward a predominance of pectoral elements. In contrast with the Anatidae, however, legs were also brought to the site

Skeletal Elements	Coturnix coturnix	Francolinus francolinus	Alectoris chukar	Ammoperdix heyi	Francolinus+Alectoris + Ammoperdix	Phasianidae Total
Coracoid	35 (28.92%)	10 (62.50%)	-	2 (50%)	12 (54.54%)	47 (25.54%)
Sternum	34 (28.10%)	1 (6.25%)	-	-	1 (4.54%)	35 (19.02%)
Scapula	1 (0.83%)	-	-	-	-	1 (0.54%)
Furcula	2 (1.65%)	-	1 (33.33%)	-	1 (4.54%)	3 (1.63%)
Humerus	11 (9.09%)	-	-	1 (25%)	1 (4.54%)	12 (6.52%)
Ulna	1 (0.83%)	1 (6.25%)	-	-	1 (4.54%)	2 (1.09%)
Carpometacarpus	2 (1.65%)	1 (6.25%)	-	-	1 (4.54%)	3 (1.63%)
Femur	5 (4.13%)	1 (6.25%)	-	-	-	6 (3.26%)
Tibiotarsus	18 (14.88%)	-	1 (33.33%)	-	1 (4.54%)	19 (10.33%)
Tarsometatarsus	12 (9.92%)	2 (12.50%)	1 (33.33%)	1 (25%)	4 (16.66%)	16 (8.70%)
Total	**121**	**16**	**3**	**4**	**22**	**184**
M.N.I.	**34** (=34 sterni)	**5** (=10/2 corac.)	**1**	**2** (=2/1 corac.)	(7)	**41**
Total Weight Estimation (kg)*	34x100=**3.400**	5x425= **2.125**	1x475= **0.475**	1x145= **0.145**	(**2.745**)	**6.145**

Table 15

Number of skeletal elements and their percentage representation in the family Phasianidae and the minimum number of individuals (MNI). Assuming that each hunted individual reflects a complete carcass consumed in the site, the meat/weight estimation is also represented. Weights of the phasianid birds were taken from Cramp and Simmons 1980.

*Weight of *Alectoris chukar*: 450-500 gr (x=475).

*Weight of *Francolinus francolinus*: 400-450 gr (x=425).

*Weight of *Coturnix coturnix*: 100 gr (x=100).

*Weight of *Ammoperdix heyi*: 140- 150 gr (x=145).

although in relatively smaller quantities. The retrieval of coracoids, sterni, and humeri may indicate intensive use of the pectoral muscles. All the other wing elements—the ulnae, radii, and carpometacarpi to which the primaries and secondaries are attached—are absent from the record. In view of the relatively unimpressive flight feathers of quails, this absence makes sense. Also missing from the record are skulls and synsacrae. Tibiotarsi and tarsometatarsi are relatively common and may indicate the usage of "drum sticks" as a favorite source of food.

The total meat recovery from the phasianids amounts to 6.145 kg (table 15) of which 3.4 kg came from quail. However, quail are the smallest known game birds, and their MNI was 34 out of 41 phasianids.

Measurements of some skeletal elements of the Netiv Hagdud population are shown in table 17 in comparison with some Natufian samples from Hayonim Cave (Pichon 1984, 1987) and some recent specimens. These measurements are displayed in order to provide a basis for comparison with other Epipaleolithic, Neolithic, and recent material, as changes in body size and other morphological changes could have taken place during the Holocene.

Francolinus francolinus	N E T I V					H A G D U D					Recent	
	Min.	Max.	x	∂	Var.	v	Std.Error	n	95% Lower	95% Upper	Mean	n
Elements												
Coracoid												
Greatest Length	39.11	41.01	39.793	1.056	1.116	2.655	0.610	3	37.169	42.417	38.41	1
Lesser Length	38.06	39.56	38.710	0.770	0.593	1.988	0.444	3	36.798	40.622	36.42	1
Tip of Proc. Procoracoideum to Prox. End of Acrocoracoideum	12.33	12.98	12.645	0.323	0.104	2.554	0.161	4	12.131	13.159	11.60	1
Alectoris graeca	-	-	-	-	-	-	-	-	-	-	-	-
Tarsometatarsus	-	-	-	-	-	-	-	-	-	-	-	-
Width of Distal End	-	-	7.660	-	-	-	-	-	-	-	-	-
Alectoris graeca (Recent)	-	-	-	-	-	-	-	-	-	-	-	-
Tarsometatarsus	-	-	-	-	-	-	-	-	-	-	-	-
Width of Distal End (male)	9.00	10.50	9.830	0.400	-	4.060	-	14	-	-	-	-
Width of Distal End (female)	9.00	9.90	9.290	0.320	-	3.440	-	6	-	-	-	-

Table 16

Measurements (in mm) of several skeletal elements remains of Phasianidae compared with populations.

n = number of specimens studied, x = mean, ∂ = Standard deviation, v = coefficient of variation, min = minimum value observed, max = maximum value observed, 95% lower = 95% confidence interval of the mean, 95% upper = 95% confidence interval of the mean.

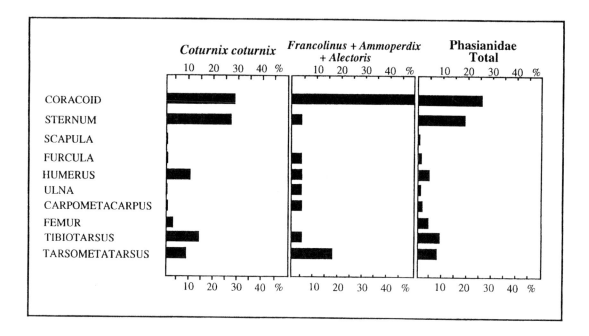

Figure 7
Relative representation of skeletal parts of several species of Phasianidae. There is a clear preference for the coracoid (as well as all the "triosseum" complex), probably indicating a special exploitation of the pectoral muscles. The distal part of the tarsometatarsus of *Alectoris chukar* was intensively used during the Natufian period for manufacturing beads (Pichon 1984).

In Zawi Chemi Shanidar (10,879 ± 300), Solecki and McGovern (1980) mentioned the existence of large raptors and a bustard—*Gypaetus barbatus, Gyps fulvus* (vultures); *Haliaeetus albicilla* (eagle); and *Otis tarda* (bustard)—from which mainly wing skeletal elements were identified. This may suggest a usage of the primaries for decoration and/or ritual purposes. The relative frequencies of the skeletal elements of raptors and bustards from Netiv Hagdud are less biased towards wing elements and suggest a multi-purpose usage of the hunted birds.

Strigiformes

Strigidae
Athene noctua (Scopoli, 1769)
This owl ranges throughout central and southern Palearctic, and well into the Saharo-Arabian belt. In the southern Levant it occupies predominantly the xero-Mediterranean and semi-arid regions, and displays more terrestrial habits than many other owls, preferring rocky open country. Today, it is very common around the Central and Lower Jordan Valley. Except for short dispersals during the winter period, it

is essentially a resident throughout its range and usually settles within 20 km of its birthplace. Preying largely on small mammals, birds, reptiles, and large insects, its hunting period is mainly at dusk.

The record is restricted to three finds, all derived from the Middle Complex and all coming from distal ends of tibiotarsi.

Passeriformes

Except for Corvidae, relatively few bones of the small passeriform birds were found in the mound. The deposition of these birds at the site could have been accidental; they could have come in the form of the regurgitation of birds of prey, through the agency of other predators, or as part of the biocoenosis. Except in the case of the crested lark, *Galerida cristata*, (see below) they do not appear to have had a special purpose or use.

Although the frequency of bones is not evenly divided among the different skeletal elements (table 18) and species (table 19), there is no straightforward explanation for this pattern of distribution, even if

Coturnix coturnix		N E T I V			H A G D U D						Recent	
	Min.	Max.	x	∂	Var.	v	Std.Error	n	95% Lower	95% Upper	Mean	n
Elements												
Tarsometatarsus												
Width of Distal End	4.88	5.13	4.97	0.139	0.019	2.795	0.080	3	4.625	5.315	5.05	1
Width of Proximal End	4.81	4.96	4.90	0.079	0.006	1.62	0.046	3	4.703	5.097	4.83	1
		H A Y O N I M		C A V E		(NATUFIAN)						
Tarsometatarsus												
Width of Distal End	4.80	5.30	5.10	0.163	O.O27	3.202	0.062	7	4.949	5.251	-	-
Width of Proximal End	4.85	5.10	4.97	0.177	0.031	3.553	0.125	2	3.387	6.563	-	-
Tibiotarsus		N E T I V			H A G D U D						Recent	
Width of Distal End	4.12	4.68	4.40	0.146	0.021	3.312	0.040	13	4.312	4.488	4.09	2
		H A Y O N I M		C A V E		(NATUFIAN)						
Tibiotarsus												
Width of Distal End	4.4	4.6	4.475	0.096	0.009	2.140	0.048	4	4.323	4.627	-	-
Coracoid		N E T I V			H A G D U D						Recent	
Greatest Length	22.08	25.03	23.806	0.903	0.816	3.795	0.319	8	23.051	24.562	23.360	2
Lesser Length	21.83	23.68	22.692	0.646	0.417	2.847	0.264	6	22.014	23.370	22.620	3
Tip of Proc. Procoracoideum to Prox. End of Acrocoracoideum	6.74	7.44	7.162	0.191	0.036	2.664	0.055	12	7.041	7.284	7.284	3
Coracoid		H A Y O N I M		C A V E		(NATUFIAN)						
Greatest Length	23.20	23.30	23.250	0.071	0.005	0.304	0.050	2	22.615	23.885	-	-
Lesser Length	22.20	22.70	22.500	0.265	0.007	0.176	0.153	3	21.843	23.157	-	-
Humerus		N E T I V			H A G D U D						Recent	
Width of Proximal End	5.48	5.49	5.650	0.231	0.053	4.090	0.116	4	5.282	6.018	-	-
Width of Distal End	7.89	8.18	8.038	0.113	0.013	1.401	0.050	5	7.898	8.178	-	-
Humerus		H A Y O N I M		C A V E		(NATUFIAN)						
Width of Proximal End	5.4	5.60	5.515	0.085	0.007	1.549	0.043	4	5.377	5.648	-	-
Width of Distal End	-	-	7.500	-	-	-	-	1	-	-	-	-

Table 17
Measurements (in mm) of several skeletal elements remains of *Coturnix coturnix* (quail) compared with Natufian (Pichon 1984) and recent populations.
n = number of specimens studied, x = mean, ∂ = Standard deviation, v = coefficient of variation, min = minimum value observed, max = maximum value observed, 95% lower = 95% confidence interval of the mean, 95% upper = 95% confidence interval of the mean.

other agents (such as owls, raptors, or carnivores) were involved in importing them into the site.

The great majority of remains were uncovered from the Middle Complex (table 19), only a few bones were found in the Lower and Upper Complex, and none were found in the Upper Area.

Alaudidae
Galerida cristata (Linnaeus, 1758)
Essentially a circum-Mediterranean species that mainly occupies the temperate regions of Europe and the Levant, the crested lark is resident in most places except in the northern part of its distribution, where it exhibits slight dispersal and immigration. It inhabits flat grasslands to semiarid country, preferring open or hillside landscape with scattered shrubs, and feeds on seeds, green parts of plants, and insects. While absent from the assemblage, today *Ammomanes deserti* is the dominant lark in the area.

Seven out of eight bones wcrc retrieved from the Middle Complex (table 19) and only one from the Upper Complex. Most of the finds are sterni and coracoids, suggesting the possibility, in this case, that crested larks were hunted intentionally for food.

Melanocorypha calandra (Linnaeus, 1766)
The calandra lark is present in the circum-Mediterranean and Levant areas, where it mainly occupies dry grasslands, with heath- and maquis- type vegetation. It is found mostly on montane steppes with stony soils and shrub growth. (Its diet is the same as the crested lark). Only partially migrant, its range extends in winter to Egypt and Arabia, and at present it is seldom found in the Netiv Hagdud area. Two sterni and a carpometacarpus were found in the Middle Complex (table 19).

Pycnonotidae
Pycnonotus xanthopygos (Hemprish and Ehrenberg, 1833)
A Levantine resident, the yellow-vented bulbul has been known from the Jordan Valley since the Lower

SKELETAL ELEMENTS	NUMBER	PERCENTAGE
Coracoid	13	25.00
Sternum	9	17.30
Furcula	1	1.92
Scapula	1	1.92
Humerus	5	9.60
Ulna	4	7.70
Carpometacarpus	5	9.60
Femur	2	3.83
Tibiotarsus	9	17.30
Tarsometatarsus	3	5.60
Total	**52**	

Table 18
Frequency of skeletal elements of all (identified
and nonidentified) Passeriformes, excluding Corvidae.

Pleistocene (Tchernov 1980). As a facultative, frugiv-
orous bird, it needs access to fruits throughout the
year. Thus, in earlier periods its distribution covered
mainly oases, watered wadis, and Sudanese vegetation enclaves.

The record from Netiv Hagdud is restricted to one
sternum from the Middle Complex (table 19).

Laniidae
Lanius excubitor Linnaeus, 1758
A western Palearctic bird, the great grey shrike breeds
in the drier subarctic regions to the Sudanese regions
and winters in the more temperate to tropical zones.
In most places of the southern Levant this species is
known as resident, passage migrant, and winter visitor. Throughout this region it essentially occupies dry
open country, loosely covered with thorny trees and
bushes like *Zizyphus*, and preys on large insects and
small vertebrates. Today it is common all along the
Jordan Rift Valley.

Finds are confined to a single ulna derived from the
Middle Complex (table 19).

Turdidae
Turdus merula Linnaeus, 1758
The blackbird is essentially a Palearctic resident and
migrant species that breeds mainly in warmer boreal
to warm temperate zones. In the southern Levant,
breeding and migrant populations are known to
replace each other during the migratory periods or to
overlap during the winter. It is mainly found in all
types of forest-edge with undergrowth and feeds on
insects, earthworms, snails, and berries. It is currently absent from the Lower Jordan Valley and Dead Sea
area.

The record is confined to two items from the Middle
Complex (table 19).

Fringillidae
Serinus serinus (Linnaeus, 1758)
Highly graminivorous, with a breeding region covering the circum-Mediterranean region and the temperate part of Europe, this species is known as a common
winter visitor in the Levant. During the breeding period and the winter, the serin is found mainly in forest
edges, parkland, and bush country. Serins are very
rarely observed at present in this region during the
migratory season.

Finds are confined to two items, both from the
Lower Complex (table 19).

Coccothraustes coccothraustes (Linnaeus, 1758)
In the western Palearctic, the breeding area of this
species covers mainly the temperate zones, while its
winter resorts are mainly in the southern belt of the
southern Palearctic. Chiefly arboreal, it occupies
mixed woodland and parks. Migration is erratic and
may be linked to some extent with availability of food
(fruit stones and pips, hard seeds of various deciduous trees, some tree insects). At present it is absent
from the Lower Jordan Valley.

Two skeletal elements (sternum and carpometacarpus, table 19) were found in the Middle Complex.

cf. Fringilla sp.
One sternum was retrieved from the Middle Complex
(table 19).

Ploceidae
Passer domesticus (Linnaeus, 1758)
Although finds are confined to one coracoid that was
uncovered from the Middle Complex of the site (table
19), the existence of this species in the area is of inter-
est.

The house sparrow is an ubiquitous commensal of
humans. Almost invariably throughout its range, it is
very closely linked with human habitations. *Passer pre-
domesticus* is an extinct sparrow which was first identified from the Late Acheulian faunal-bearing beds of
Oumm-Qatafa (Judean Desert; Tchernov 1962) and
may represent the ancestral form of the modern
house sparrow. During the Upper Pleistocene only a
few specimens were found and could have been
assigned as intermediate stages between the two
species. However, the predominance of *Passer domesti-*

AREA	DEEP SOUNDING			UPPER AREA	Total
Element | Complex	Lower complex	Middle Complex	Upper Complex		
Alaudidae					
Galerida cristata					
Coracoid	-	2(2l)(p);	1(r)(p);	-	3
Sternum	-	3(p);	-	-	3
Humerus	-	1(r)(p);	-	-	1
Carpometacarpus		1(l)(c);	-	-	1
Total	0	7	1	0	(8)
Melanocorypha calandra					
Sternum	-	2(p);	-	-	2
Carpometacarpus	-	1(l)(c);	-	-	1
Total	0	3	0	0	(3)
Pycnonotidae					
Pycnonotus xanthopygos					
Sternum	-	1(p);	-	-	1
Total	0	1	0	0	(1)
Laniidae					
Lanius excubitor					
Ulna	-	1(r)(c);	-	-	1
Total	0	1	0	0	(1)
Turdidae					
Turdus merula					
Coracoid	-	1(l)(p);	-	-	1
Humerus	-	1(r)(d);	-	-	1
Total	0	2	0	0	(2)
Fringillidae					
cf. *Fringilla* sp.					
Sternum		1(p);	-	-	1
Total	0	1	0	0	(1)
Serinus serinus					
Coracoid	1(r)(c);	-	-	-	1
Humerus	1(l)(c);	-	-	-	1
Total	2	0	0	0	(2)
Coccothraustes coccothraustes					
Sternum	-	1(p);	-	-	1
Carpometacarpus	-	1(l)(c);	-	-	1
Total	0	2	0	0	(2)
Ploceidae					
Passer domesticus					
Coracoid	-	1(l)(c);	-	-	1
Total	0	1	0	0	(1)
Sturnidae					
Sturnus vulgaris					
Coracoid	-	-	1(l)(c);	-	1
Humerus	1(r)(c);	-	-	-	1
Total	1	0	1	0	(2)
Onychognathus tristrami					
Coracoid	-	-	1(r)(p);	-	1
Total	0	0	1	0	(1)
Passeriformes Undetermined					
Coracoid	1(l)(d);	1(l)(c); 2(r+l)(d);	1(l)(c);	-	5
Sternum	-	1(p);	-	-	1
Furcula	-	1(p);	-	-	1
Scapula	-	1(l)(p);	-	-	1
Humerus	-	1(r)(d);	-	-	1
Ulna	1(l)(d);	1(l)(d); 1(r)(p);	-	-	3
Carpometacarpus	-	1(r)(d); 1(l)(p);	-	-	2
Femur	-	2(l)(d);	-	-	2
Tibiotarsus	2(l+r)(d); 1(l)(p);	1(r)(p); 4(2r+2l)(d);	1(r)(d);	-	9
Tarsometatarsus	-	3(2r+l)(d);	-	-	3
Total	5	21	2	0	(28)
Grand Total	8	39	5	0	52

Table 19
Inventory of Passeriformes (excluding Corvidae) remains, representation of their skeletal elements and their distribution along the sequence.
c= complete; l= left; r= right; p= proximal; d=distal.

cus in the Natufian layers of Hayonim Cave (Pichon 1984, 1989), where it constitutes more than 50 percent of all avian remains, and its striking morphological similarity to the recent house sparrow, show that the species underwent profound changes during this period. The preadapted behavioral and morphological characters enabled it to be a successful colonizer. Consequently it invaded the insular and unique anthropogenic Natufian habitats. During the Natufian (and ever since then), it became one of the most, and sometimes the only, dominant species in human habitations, representing an example par excellence of obligatory commensal relationship between humans and another modern vertebrate species (Tchernov 1984, 1991a, 1991b).

The Netiv Hagdud area does not provide a sustainable habitat for this species. Without some artificial support *Passer domesticus* would not have survived in this area. Therefore the existence of the house sparrow in this place indicates a long-term occupation of the area that offered sufficient food refuse and enough protected nest sites to support the species.

Sturnidae

Sturnus vulgaris Linnaeus, 1758

It is indeed unexpected to find the remains of starlings at Netiv Hagdud, as this trans-Palearctic (and recently Nearctic) species is a winter visitor in the southern Palearctic region that has to roost during nights on large trees and forage during the day in wet grasslands and meadows. It feeds mostly on seeds and terrestrial invertebrates.

A coracoid and a humerus were found in the Lower and Upper Complex (table 19).

Onychognathus tristrami (P. Sclater, 1858)

An Arabian species of Ethiopian origin with great antiquity in the southern Levant (Tchernov 1988), Tristram's grackle has been known as a resident throughout its distribution with some slight winter dispersal.

The species occupies rocky hills and ravines, chiefly along the Syro-Arabian Rift Valley in desert and semi-desert regions, but usually is not far from water sources or oases, and is considered an omnivore.

The fossil record is confined to one coracoid from the Upper Complex (table 19). Tristram's grackle is common at present throughout the Dead Sea area.

Corvidae

This group is represented by five species and constitutes one of the most abundant avian groups in the assemblage (355 bones, table 20). Particularly common is the hooded crow, *Corvus corone*, of the *cornix* group (325 bones). Apparently this group, and in particular the hooded crow, played an important role in the socioeconomic strategy of the local people. Hunting crows, ravens, and magpies is a highly demanding task and would have required sophisticated and specialized methods, elaborate devices and practice, as well as significant knowledge of the bird's life and behavior.

The stratigraphic distribution of the Corvidae along the sequence (table 20) shows that the highest quantities were retrieved from the Middle Complex of the Deep Sounding, fewer in the Lower Complex, only two bones in the Upper Complex, and six in the Upper Area. However, the frequency of bones per volume (m³) shows that the richest layer is the Lower Complex:

1. The Lower Complex yielded 19 bones per m³.
2. The Middle Complex yielded 18 bones per m³.
3. The Upper Complex yielded 0.66 bones per m³.
4. The Upper Area yielded 0.047 bones per m³.

Percentage representation of the skeletal elements of the various species and of the group as a whole is given in table 21 and figure 8. The relative representation of the different skeletal elements is conspicuously skewed toward elements connected with the pectoral girdle, mainly the coracoid, much the same as was found in the Anatidae (figs. 3, 4). The relatively few elements of the rear parts of the body are mainly represented by tarsometatarsi. Skull parts were also rarely retrieved, represented by a few upper and lower jaws and two quadrati.

The abundance of the pectoral elements seems to indicate, as with some other avian groups, a high preference for the pectoral muscles. The hunters apparently did not bother to carry the whole carcass back to the site and, as a rule, left the posterior parts of the body as well as the head at the hunting site. Much as with other previously mentioned groups (Anatidae, some of the Phasianidae), the inhabitants of Netiv Hagdud were very pedantic about selecting only the fleshiest bones of these birds. Figure 8 shows the discrepancy in the abundance of the skeletal parts within the Corvidae. Yet again, there is no way to argue whether this preference was due to purely dietary and economic considerations or was deter-

AREA	DEEP SOUNDING			UPPER AREA	Total
Element | Complex	Lower complex	Middle Complex	Upper Complex		
Corvus cornix					
Coracoid	9(5r+4l)(d); 13(7l+6r)(p); 9(5l+4r)(c);	42(21r+21l)(p); 42(21r+21l)(d); 24(12r+12l)(c);	1(r)(p);	4(2r+2l)(p);	144
Scapula	16(8r+8l)(p); 1(l)(c);	42(20r+22l)(p);	-	1(r)(p);	60
Sternum	6(p);	25(p);	1(p);	-	32
Furcula	-	10(p);	-	1(p);	11
Humerus	3(2r+l)(p); 1(l)(d);	15(7l+8r)(p);	-	-	19
Ulna	1(r)(p);	2(r+l)(p);	-	-	3
Carpometacarpus	1(l)(p); 3(2l+r)(d);	6(3r+3l)(d); 4(2r+2l)(p);	-	-	14
Phalanx 1, wing digit III	-	1(l)(c);	-	-	1
Ilium	-	1(l)(i);	-	-	1
Femur	-	2(r)(d); 1(l)(p); 1(l)(c);	-	-	4
Tibiotarsus	-	2(r)(p); 10(6r+4l)(d);	-	-	12
Tarsometatarsus	5(3r+2l)(d);	11(6r+5l)(d); 2(2r)(p);	-	-	18
Upper Jaw	-	1(i);	-	-	1
Lower Jaw	-	2(l)(d); 1(r)(p);	-	-	3
Quadratum	-	2(?)(c);	-	-	2
Total	68	209	2	6	(285)
Corvus monedula					
Coracoid	1(l)(d); 2(l+r)(p);	4(2r+2l)(c); 2(2r)(p); 1(l)(d);	-	-	10
Scapula	3(r+2l)(p);	2(r+l)(p);	-	-	5
Sternum	2(p);	1(p);	-	-	1
Humerus	1(r)(p);	1(r)(p);	-	-	2
Carpometacarpus	1(l)(d); 2(r+l)(p);	1(r)(p);	-	-	2
Tibiotarsus	-	1(l)(d);	-	-	1
Tarsometatarsus	1(r)(p);	-	-	-	1
Lower Jaw	-	1(l)(c);	-	-	1
Total	13	14	0	0	(27)
Corvus ruficollis					
Coracoid	-	2(r)(d);	-	-	2
Total	0	2	0	0	(2)
Corvus rhipidurus					
Sternum	-	1(p);	-	-	1
Total	0	1	0	0	(1)
Pica pica					
Coracoid	1(l)(c); 1(l)(p);	2(2r+l)(p);	-	-	4
Tarsometatarsus	1(r)(d);	-	-	-	1
Total	3	2	0	0	(5)
Grand Total	84	228	2	6	320

Table 20
Inventory of Corvidae remains, representation of their skeletal elements, and their distribution along the sequence.
c= complete; i= incomplete; l= left; r= right; p= proximal; d=distal; ?= side unknown.

mined by other cultural factors. Among the posterior parts the tarsometatarsus is the most common element (table 21, fig. 8), and being a fleshless element, must have been used for non-dietary purposes. Table 21 also shows the amount of meat that could have been extracted from each one of the species and from the Corvidae as a unit.

Corvus corone cornix Linnaeus, 1758

The distribution of the cornix group covers the warm temperate Palearctic region where it mostly occupies woodlands, parklands, and open country with trees in abundance. Nests are built almost always on tall trees. In the southern Levant, the cornix is always resident and occupies a wide range of habitats, essentially within the Mediterranean and xero-Mediterranean regions. As a highly synanthropic species, in contrast with commensal species which are obligatorily dependent on human habitats (Tchernov 1984,

1991a), the hooded crow may survive in semiarid areas, but only in association with human habitation. However, throughout its distribution, its nesting sites are always found on top of tall trees.

In Netiv Hagdud the hooded crow constitutes the most abundant species in the assemblage (tables 20, 21). Its dominance in the fossil record is apparently due not only to its wide distribution in the area, but also to the fact that the local hunters especially favored its pectoral muscles (fig. 8).

The existence of this species in great abundance in this area is of a great ecological and environmental importance. Considering its essentially Mediterranean and xero-Mediterranean distribution, as well as the fact that its present distribution lies much farther to the east and to the north, its existence in the Lower Jordan Valley during the PPNA clearly indicates a basically different quality of habitats than exist there today. Conditions must have been much

Skeletal Elements	Corvus corone cornix	Corvus monedula	Corvus ruficollis	Corvus rhipidurus	Pica pica	Corvidae Total
Coracoid	144 (44.31%)	10 (43.48%)	2 (100%)	-	4 (100%)	160 (45.07%)
Scapula	60 (18.46%)	5 (21.74%)	-	-	-	65 (18.31%)
Sternum	32 (9.85%)	1 (4.34%)	-	1 (100%)	-	34 (9.58%)
Furcula	11 (3.38%)	-	-	-	-	11 (3.10%)
Humerus	19 (5.84%)	2 (8.69%)	-	-	-	21 (5.91%)
Ulna	3 (0.92%)	-	-	-	-	3 (0.84%)
Carpometacarpus	14 (4.31%)	2 (8.69%)	-	-	-	16 (4.54%)
Phalanx 1,wing digit III	1 (0.31%)	-	-	-	-	1 (0.28%)
Ilium	1 (0.31%)	-	-	-	-	1 (0.28%)
Femur	4 (1.23%)	-	-	-	-	4 (1.13%)
Tibiotarsus	12 (3.69%)	1 (4.34%)	-	-	-	13 (3.66%)
Tarsometatarsus	18 (5.54%)	1 (4.34%)	-	-	-	19 (5.35%)
Upper Jaw	1 (0.31%)	-	-	-	-	1 (0.28%)
Lower Jaw	3 (0.92%)	1 (4.34%)	-	-	-	4 (1.13%)
Quadratum	2 (0.62%)	-	-	-	-	2 (0.56%)
Total	325	23	2	1	4	**Grand Total: 355**
M.N.I.	**72** (=144/2 corac.)	**5** (=10/2 corac.)	**1** (=2/1 corac.)	**1**	**2** (=4/2 corac.)	**80** (=160/2 corac.)
Total Weight Estimation (kg)*	72x395= **28.440**	5x240= **1.200**	**0.675**	**0.440**	2x175= **0.350**	**Total: 31.105**

Table 21
Number of skeletal elements and their percentage representation in the family Corvidae and the minimum number of individuals (MNI). Assuming that each hunted individual reflects a complete carcass consumed in the site, the meat/weight estimation is also represented. Weights of the Corvidae were recorded by the author.

*Weight of *Corvus corone cornix*: 330–460 gr (x=395).
*Weight of *Corvus monedula*: 190–290 gr (x=240).
*Weight of *Corvus ruficollis*: 500–850 gr (x=675).
*Weight of *Corvus rhipidurus*: 330–550 gr (x=440).
*Weight of *Pica pica*: 150–200 gr (x= 175).

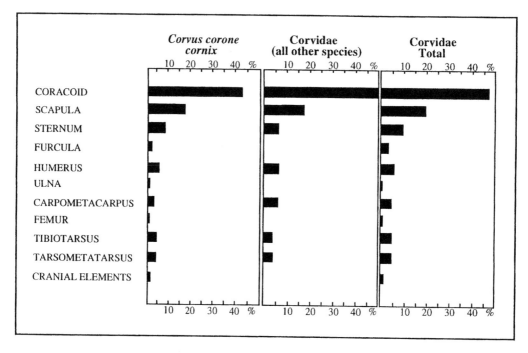

Figure 8
Relative representation of skeletal parts of Corvidae, mainly *Corvus corone* from the PPNA of Netiv Hagdud. There is a conspicuous preference for the "triosseum" complex, or the pectoral muscles of this group which was heavily exploited by the community of Netiv Hagdud.

wetter and/or cooler in order to allow tall trees to grow there numerously enough to support the large nest sites needed to explain the dominance of this species in the assemblage. Although they are often colonial foragers and may aggregate for various social functions, they are solitary breeders, and their territories are highly spaced. As a very generalist, omnivorous, and synanthropic species, the local population of crows probably took advantage of the refuse and low species diversity around the site (Tchernov 1991a, 1991b). Moreover, as a close associate with anthropogenic environments, its existence in such abundance in this area may also indicate a long-term human habitation (Lieberman 1993).

An attempt to compare the skeletal morphology of the PPNA crows from Netiv Hagdud with the recent population from the Jerusalem area (table 22) shows a certain segregation in one morphological trait of the coracoid. As the sample of coracoids from the PPNA population was large enough, three variables were compared with the recent specimens (figs. 9, 10, 11). However, the recent material is too small to firmly substantiate the results. While no visible differences can be noted in figure 11 where the "Greater Length of Coracoid" is plotted against the "Lesser Length of Coracoid," the two other scatter diagrams (figs. 9, 10) show the two recent specimens conspicuously separated from the PPNA population. In this case the "Lesser" and "Greater Length of Coracoid" were plotted against the "Distance from Tip of Proc. Procoracoideum to Prox. End of Acrocoracoideum," which shows that this trait changed during the Holocene or that

some differences existed between the Neolithic population of the Lower Jordan Valley and the recent population from the Jerusalem area. However, none of the coracoid variables have shown significant differences between the populations using paired t-test. For the "Distance from Tip of Proc. Procoracoideum to Prox. End of Acrocoracoid," p=0.336; for the "Lesser Length of Coracoid," p=0.597; and for the "Greater Length of Coracoid," p= 0.448.

Corvus ruficollis Lesson, 1831
A typical Saharo-Arabian species, the brown-necked raven is very abundant in a variety of terrains that includes *Artemisia* steppes, barren hilly areas, desert and semi-desert scrub or trees, oases, and rock ledges. Much as with *Corvus corone cornix*, however, it is a highly synanthropic species and is found sometimes in large aggregations around human habitations. In the light of its great abundance today in the area, it is surprising to find this species represented by only two coracoids (tables 20, 21).

Corvus rhipidurus Hartert, 1918
The distribution of the fan-tailed raven generally covers the Dead Sea–African Rift Valley. Within this mainly north-south lengthwise geographical stretch, it is fragmented into many semi-isolated populations but is very abundant around the Dead Sea, where it inhabits crags and cliffs. Very gregarious, highly synanthropic, and a highly omnivorous species, it is found in large flocks around rubbish.

Corvus corone cornix			N E T I V			H A G	D U D				R E C E N T			
	Min.	Max.	x	∂	Var.	v	Std.Error	n	95% Lower	95% Upper	Min.	Max.	x	n
Elements														
Carpometacarpus														
Width of Distal End	10.030	11.330	10.480	0.737	0.543	7.028	0.425	3	8.65	12.310	10.300	10.560	10.420	3
Width of Proximal End	10.003	11.580	10.932	0.686	0.471	6.276	0.307	5	10.08	11.784	11.53	12.160	11.773	3
Diameter of Trochlea Carpalis	5.650	5.890	5.800	0.131	0.017	2.225	0.075	3	5.475	6.125	6.14	6.240	6.203	3
Humerus														
Width of Proximal End	16.380	18.300	17.693	0.548	0.300	3.095	0.173	10	17.301	18.085	16.6	18.580	17.847	3
Width of Distal End	-	-	13.650	-	-	-	-	1	-	-	14.38	14.760	14.587	3
Coracoid														
Greatest Length	40.290	45.720	42.350	1.448	2.095	3.421	0.312	21	41.651	42.969	43.280	45.640	44.460	2
Lesser Length	37.750	42.700	39.633	1.322	1.747	3.335	0.264	25	39.087	40.179	39.350	42.000	40.675	2
Tip of Proc. Procoracoideum to Prox. End of Acrocoracoideum	13.570	17.24	14.877	3.375	11.394	22.689	0.492	47	13.886	15.869	13.020	18.580	15.800	2
Tibiotarsus														
Width of Distal End	7.770	8.57	8.224	1.291	0.085	5.357	0.110	7	7.455	8.443	7.990	8.580	8.313	4
Tarsometatarsus														
Width of Distal End	6.590	7.330	6.930	0.219	0.048	3.158	0.073	9	6.762	7.098	6.750	7.190	7.000	4
Width of Proximal End	6.730	8.360	7.235	0.760	0.577	10.499	0.380	4	6.026	8.444	8.670	10.030	9.310	4

Table 22
Measurements (in mm) of several skeletal elements remains of *Corvus corone cornix* compared with a few recent specimens. n = number of specimens studied, x = mean, ∂ = Standard deviation, v = coefficient of variation, min = minimum value observed, max = maximum value observed, 95% lower = 95% confidence interval of the mean, 95% upper = 95% confidence interval of the mean.

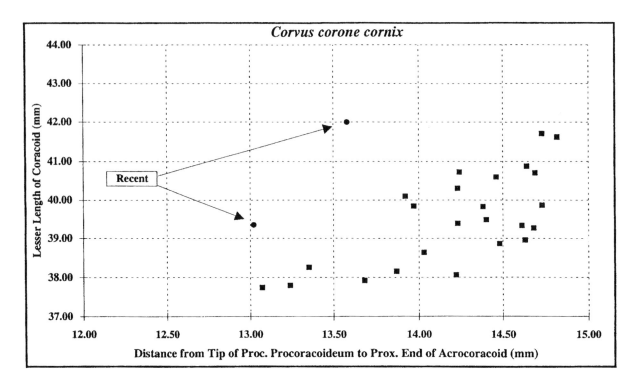

Figure 9
Plot of two variables of the coracoid comparing *Corvus corone cornix* from Netiv Hagdud with a few individuals from the Jerusalem region. The recent population shows a significantly smaller size compared with the PPNA crows.

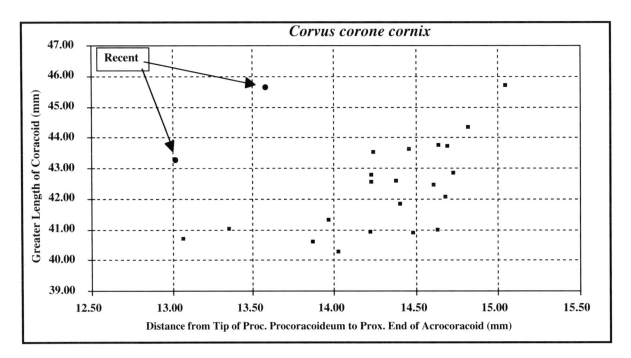

Figure 10
Plot of two variables of the coracoid comparing *Corvus corone cornix* from Netiv Hagdud with a few individuals from the Jerusalem region. The recent population shows a significantly smaller size compared with the PPNA crows.

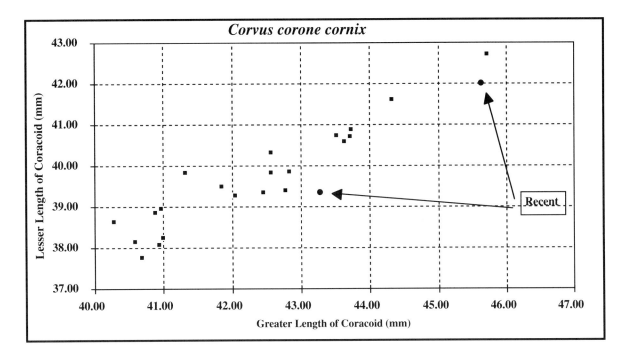

Figure 11
Plot of two variables of the coracoid comparing *Corvus corone cornix* from Netiv Hagdud with a few individuals from the Jerusalem region. There are no visible differences between the two populations in these traits.

Being so common at present around the Dead Sea, its rarity in the assemblage (confined to one sternum, tables 20, 21) raises some questions. The only reasonable explanation for the rarity of both *Corvus ruficollis* and *Corvus rhipidurus* during the Neolithic, as reflected by the avian record on Netiv Hagdud, and in contrast with their present abundance and dominance in the area, is the sympatric existence of *Corvus corone cornix*. Due to its aggressive nature (heavy mobbing and other socially aggressive behavior), *Corvus corone cornix* could have excluded other species from the area. Once the hooded crow, as well as *Corvus monedula* (see below), retreated northeastward during the early Holocene, its wide ecological niche was probably occupied immediately by these two species.

Corvus monedula Linnaeus, 1758
A Palearctic species, jackdaw populations from the northern ranges are migrants while those from the southern ranges are mainly residents. Migration is limited to the southern Palearctic zone, and they do not penetrate to the Saharo-Arabian desert belt. Thus both resident populations and winter visitors of the same species occupy the southern Levant.

This bird feeds mostly on the ground in open areas, but requires well-grown trees or rock outcrops for roosting and nesting mainly gregariously in holes. At present only a few colonies are known as residents from the hills of Judea and Somera.

Twenty-three bones (mostly coracoids and scapulae) were identified (tables 20, 21), indicating a relatively high abundance of this species. There is no way to decide, however, whether the local populations of jackdaw were residents, winter visitors, or both. In any case, as this species utterly avoids Eremian habitats, its existence in this area during the PPNA indicates once more that the whole region must have been much more mesic than today.

Pica pica (Linnaeus, 1758)
The record of the magpie (together with *Arvicola terrestris*, see below) within the assemblage of Netiv Hagdud is probably the most surprising find from this site. This is a Palearctic species but is unknown at present in the southern Levant, with the exception of one isolated population south of Mecca, Saudi-Arabia (Tchernov 1981, 1988). There are, however, some fossil records of this species from several Upper Pleistocene sites, but in particular from Natufian sites

(Tchernov 1962; Bar-Yosef and Tchernov 1966; Pichon 1984, 1987, 1989). The existence of *Pica pica* in this area during the PPNA shows that those Palearctic species that retreated farther northward during the Holocene still found suitable habitats in which to survive in areas that are at present extremely arid. It was probably only after the PPNA (and PPNB?) that these species became extinct in this region. The intensive pleniglacial desiccation and the swift temperature increase caused an overall regression of the Palearctic elements from the southern Levant. Those populations which were left behind (such as *Pica pica asirensis* in Arabia, Tchernov 1981, 1988) continued to survive thereafter on a very delicate ecological baseline in refugional enclaves, mostly on the high mountains of the Saharo-Arabian-Eremian belt.

An omnivorous bird, the typical habitat of the magpie is dense shrubs and trees to open country with tall trees (parkland), scattered woods, pine- and juniper-covered slopes. The species is essentially resident throughout its distribution. There is no way to explain the existence of this species just north of the Dead Sea, except through completely different climatic conditions in the area capable of supporting at least an open parkland habitat during the PPNA.

Four coracoids were retrieved from the avian assemblage (tables 20, 21), showing that this bird, like the other corvids, was mainly exploited for its pectoral muscles as a source of rich food.

Unidentified Species of Birds

Unidentified bone remains amount to 1,311 items (table 23). Many are too fragmentary even for the diagnosis of the skeletal element. Some elements, like vertebrae, scapulae, and phalanxes are much less diagnostic than other elements, making identifications difficult. However, the major part of the unidentified material seems to belong to the Anatidae and the Corvidae.

Mammalia

Insectivora

Erinaceidae
In comparison with all other southern Levantine sites, the abundance of hedgehogs in Netiv Hagdud (5

percent) is conspicuously above the normal recorded relative frequencies (0.1–1 percent). The reason for the unexpected abundance of this group is not clear; it may be due to human preferences or predator activities or both. The high representation of this group may be also explained by the astonishing fact that all three hedgehog species from the southern Levant coexisted in the area. There is at present no other place in the Middle East where these three are sympatric. Being highly insectivorous, they must have been supported by an exceptionally large variety of insect species. They probably also attracted different predators, probably including humans, that became more specialized in feeding on them.

The distribution of the different species in the deposits is given in table 24. Most of the remains were retrieved from the Middle Complex and none from the Upper Area.

Erinaceus concolor Martin, 1838
A trans-Palearctic species and a member of the boreal Eurasian fauna which extends into the higher rainfall regions of southern Levant (Harrison and Bates 1991), *Erinaceus concolor* occupies typical Mediterranean landscapes, and is usually found in deciduous forest, and wooded steppe and agricultural areas.

Hemiechinus auritus (Gmelin, 1770)
Essentially Irano-Turanian, this species ranges across Asia to North Africa, from Cyrenaica to China. Within the southern Levantine region this species does not seem to occupy true deserts, but rather frequents semiarid terrain. It displays a more or less parapatric pattern of distribution between *Erinaceus concolor* and *Paraechinus aethiopicus*.

Paraechinus aethiopicus (Ehrenberg, 1833)
A Saharo-Arabian and Ethiopian species, this hedgehog is at present only marginally sympatric with *Hemiechinus auratus* in the Levant where it occupies the arid parts of the deserts. This species is the only hedgehog known at present from the Lower Jordan Valley.

Rodentia

The relative frequency of rodents in the deposits is high, and in particular the Upper and the Middle Complexes have yielded most of the material. The

AREA	D E E P S O U N D I N G			UPPER AREA	Total
Element | Complex	Lower complex	Middle Complex	Upper Complex		
Aves - Undetermined					
Coracoid	**5**(2r+3l)(p); **6**(3r+2l)(d);	**59**(29l+30r)(d); **46**(23r+23l)(p);	**6**(2l+4r)(p); **2**(2l)(d);	**3**(2r+l)(p);	127
Sternum	**23**(p);	**112**(p);	**4**(p);	**1**(p);	140
Scapula	**22**(10r+12l)(p);	**22**(?)(p);	**3**(?)(p);	-	47
Furcula	**4**(p);	**27**(p);	**3**(p);	-	34
Humerus	**6**(3l+3r)(p); **8**(4l+4r)(d);	**42**(21r+21l)(d); **35**(17+18r)(p);	-	**1**(r)(d);	92
Ulna	**4**(2r+2l)(p); **4**(2r+2l)(d);	**19**(10l+9r)(p); **18**(9r+89)(d);	**1**(r)(p);	**1**(r)(d);	47
Radius	**10**(?)(d);	**28**(14l+14r)(p); **27**(7r+7l)(d);	**2**(?)(p);	**2**(?)(p);	69
Carpometacarpus	**1**(r)(d); **5**(3l+2r)(p);	**10**(5l+5r)(c); **13**(6l+7r)(d);	**2**(r)(d);	**2**(r+l)(p);	33
Phalanx 2, wing digit II	**7**(?)(c);	**18**(?)(c);	**1**(?)(c);	-	26
Synsacrum	**7**(i);	**77**(i);	-	**1**(i);	85
Pelvis	**1**(?)(i);	**10**(?)(i);	-	-	11
Femur	**4**(2r+2l)(p);	**13**(6r+7l)(p); **8**(4r+4l)(d);	-	**1**(l)(p);	26
Tibiotarsus	**6**(3r+3l)(p); **8**(4r+4l)(d);	**20**(10r+10l)(d); **17**(8l+9r)(p);	**1**(l)(p);	**1**(l)(d);	53
Tarsometatarsus	**2**(r)(d); **1**(l)(p);	**7**(?)(i); **12**(6r+6l)(d);	-	-	22
Phalanx 1, foot digit II	**2**(C);	**12**(?)(C); **8**(?)(i);	-	-	22
Phalanx 3, foot digit I	-	**9**(?)(c);	-	**1**(?)(c);	10
Upper Jaw	**1**(?)(i);	-	-	-	1
Lower Jaw	**3**(?)(i);	**13**(?)(i);	**2**(?)(i);	-	18
Quadratum	**2**(c);	**7**(c);	-	**1**(c);	10
Vertebrae	**16**(c);	**89**(c);	**4**(c);	**1**(c);	110
Ribs	-	**4**(?)(p);	-	-	4
Non-Diagnostic Elements	**49**(i);	**273**(i);	**1**(i);	**1**(i);	324
Total	207	1055	32	17	1311

Table 23
Inventory of unidentified bird remains, representation of their skeletal elements, and their distribution along the sequence.
c= complete; i= incomplete; l= left; r= right; p= proximal; d=distal; ?= side unknown.

AREA	DEEP SOUNDING	DEEP SOUNDING	DEEP SOUNDING	UPPER AREA	Total
Species | Complex	Lower Complex	Middle Complex	Upper Complex		
Erinaceidae					
Paraechinus aethiopicus					
Mandible	-	**2**(i)(r+l); **1**(c)(r);	**2**(i)(r+l);	-	5
Hemiechinus auratus				-	
Mandible	**1**(i)(l);	**8**(i)(4r+4l);	**3**(i)(2r+l); **1**M_1(c).	-	13
Maxillary	-	**3**(i)(2r+l);	-	-	3
Erinaceus concolor					
Mandible	**1**(i)(l);	**5**(i)(4l+1r);	**2**(i)(r+l);	-	8
Maxillary	**1**(i)(r);	**1**(i)(r);	-	-	2
Femur	-	**1**(i)(r);	-	-	1
Erinaceidae undet.					
Lower jaw	**1**(i)(r);	-	-	-	1
Scapula	-	-	**1**(c)(r);	-	1
Total:	4	21	9	0	34

Table 24
Inventory of Erinaceidae remains, representation of their skeletal elements, and their distribution along the sequence.
c=complete; i-incomplete; l=left; r=right.

stratigraphic distribution of the group and its density along the sequence was found to be very uneven. The highest frequency per volume of matrix was found in the Middle Complex of the Deep Sounding, and the lowest in the Upper Area. The density was calculated as number of elements per m³ of matrix:

1. The Middle Complex has yielded 18,346 specimens per m³.
2. The Upper Complex has yielded 14,660 specimens per m³.
3. The Lower Complex has yielded 1.690 specimens per m³.

4. The Upper Area has yielded only 0.105 specimens per m³.

If the rodents recovered from this site constituted an in situ community, i.e., they died and were fossilized within their own burrows or natural territories, higher frequencies of rodent elements would have been expected from the higher levels, especially from the Upper Area. Only rarely will burrowing rodents dig deep enough as to reach the Middle Complex. As non-burrowing species like *Mus musculus* or semiaquatic species like *Arvicola terrestris* have shown the same pattern of distribution throughout the complexes (table 25) much as the subterranean species like *Spalax ehrenbergi* or typical burrowers like *Psammomys obesus*, it is improbable that the rodent assemblage of this site represents an autochthonous community. This is also indicated by the highly selective skeletal elements retrieved from the site. Except for one femur, all the remains are confined to maxillaries, mandibles, and isolated teeth (table 25). Therefore, it is concluded that the rodent assemblages of Netiv Hagdud represent a typical thanatocoenosis accumulation deposited by predators, mostly owls or small carnivores, that could have been active within and near the settlement. It is, however, certainly a non-anthropogenic assemblage. Nocturnal raptors are not disturbed by people or by the temporal division of the same habitat, while diurnal predators maintain a certain distance from people. As such, the rodent remains can be used as effective non-anthropogenic paleoenvironmental indicators.

Gerbillidae

Psammomys obesus Cretzschmar, 1828
The fat jird ranges across North Africa south to the Sudan and across the Arabian peninsula northward to the Syrian Desert. As a truly Eremian Saharo-Arabian monotypic and colonial species, it favors light soils and in particular low sandy mounds surrounding salty, succulent desert vegetation like *Anabasis*, *Salsola*, *Suaeda*, *Traganum*, and *Zygophyllum* on which it feeds. The complex burrows are normally surrounded by one of these succulent shrubs. Having the food resources around it, the fat jird will not forage for large distances. Therefore, predominance (table 25) of this rodent in the deposits indicates its high frequency near the site; yet it was apparently ignored by the local human population. The strong obligatory association of *Psammomys obesus* to these succulent plants (an extreme stenophagous species) may also indicate,

in contrast with the house mice (see below), its complete independence from human activities, as it did not take advantage of the anthropogenic habitat, and that its distribution could not be influenced by the size and duration of the PPNA sites in the area (Gilgal, Netiv Hagdud, and Salibiya IX).

It is worth noting that as one of the specific hosts for the fly that carries leishmaniasis, this species could have affected the local human inhabitants. This issue should be studied further in the future.

One hundred thirty-one specimens were identified (table 25) from the site and some dental variables were compared with a large sample of a local recent population of the fat jird. The measurements of some lower and upper molars, as well as the lower and upper alveolar row, are presented in table 26. Both the recent and fossil samples display an unusually wide range of variability, a phenomenon that may mask morphological and size differences between the recent and the fossil populations. Scatter diagrams of some of these variables (figs. 12, 13) show that the PPNA population from Netiv Hagdud seems to exceed the size of the recent one (Length /Width of M1: fig. 12 and Length of Lower Alveolar Row: fig. 13). The unusually high range of variability in all the measured variables from the PPNA population, in spite of their smaller number, is shown in figures 12 and 13 and may be explained by the longer period of deposition, accumulating more variants with time. However, students' *t*-tests for two-tail probabilities did not show any significant differences between the two populations (probabilities always ranged from 0.38 to 0.20 for all the tested variables: table 26). Thus, it seems that within the Lower Jordan Valley *Psammomys obesus* did not show any significant size or morphological changes during the Holocene.

Meriones tristrami Thomas, 1892
This jird occupies the whole Mediterranean belt of the southern Levant, usually never below the 300 mm isohyet or beyond the boundary of the Mediterranean vegetation which is characterized by *Sarcopoterium spinosum*, *Phlomis brachyodon*, and *Ballota undulata* (M. Zohary 1973; Danin 1988).

Forty-five maxillae, mandibles, and teeth were identified, mainly from the Middle Complex (table 25), and the range of variability agrees with the recent population of *Meriones tristrami* from the Judean area (Chetboun and Tchernov 1983). Measurements are given in table 27. Today, this species is

AREA	DEEP SOUNDING			UPPER AREA	Total
Skull Elements | Complex	Lower complex	Middle Complex	Upper Complex		
Psammnomys obesus					
Maxilla	-	6(r)(i)6(l)(i);	1(r)(i);	1(l)(c);	14
I1	-	5(c);	-	-	5
M2	-	3(c);	-	3(c);	6
M1	-	5(c);	-	1(c);	6
M3	-	1(c);	1(c);	-	2
Mandible	1(l)(i)2(r)(i);	22 (l)(i)13 (r)(i);	2(c)(i)1 (r)(i);	2(r)(i);	43
I I	1(c);	7(c);	-	1(c);	9
M 1	-	15 (c);	2(c);	2(c);	19
M 2	2(c);	18 (c);	2(c);	1(c);	23
M 3	-	3(c);	1(c);		4
Total	**6**	**104**	**10**	**11**	**131**
Meriones tristrami					
Maxilla	-	1(l)(i)3(r)(i);	1(r)(i)1(l)(i);	-	6
I1	-	3(c);	4(c);	-	7
M1	-	2(c);	-	-	2
M2	-	2(c);	-	-	2
M3	-	2(c);	-	-	2
Mandible	-	3(r)(i)4(l)(i);	2(r)(i);	-	9
I I	-	4(c);	-	-	4
M 1	-	5(c);	3(r)(i);	-	8
M 2	-	1(c);	2(r)(i);	-	3
M 3	-	1(c);	1(r)(i);	-	2
Total	**0**	**31**	**14**	**0**	**45**
Mus cf. musculus					
Maxilla	-	1(l)(i)1(r)(i);	2(l)(i)1(r)(i);	-	5
I1	-	1(c);	2(c);	-	3
M1	-	2(c);	3(c);	-	5
M2	-	2(c);	2(c);	-	4
M3	-	2(c);	-	-	2
Mandible	1(r)(i)1(l)(i);	6(l)(i)5(r)(i);	3(r)(i)1(l)(i);	-	17
I I	-	3(c);	1(c);	-	4
M 1	1(c);	10 (c);	-	-	11
M 2	1(c);	6(c);	2(c);	-	9
M 3	-	1(c);	-	-	1
Total	**4**	**40**	**17**	**0**	**61**
Spalax ehrenbergi					
Maxilla	-	1(l)(i)1(r)(i);	-	-	2
I1	-	8(c);	-	-	8
Mandible	-	6(l)(i)7(r)(i);	-	-	13
I I	1(c);	4(c);	-	-	5
M 1	-	7(c);	-	-	7
M 2	-	7(c);	-	-	7
M 3	-	5(c);	-	-	5
Total	**1**	**46**	**0**	**0**	**47**
Arvicola terrestris					
Mandible	-	1(l)(i);	-	-	1
M 1	-	1(c);	-	-	1
M 2	-	1(c);	-	-	1
M 3	-	1(c);	-	-	1
Total	**0**	**4**	**0**	**0**	**4**
Microtus guentheri					
Mandible	-	1(l)(i);	-	-	1
Total	**0**	**1**	**0**	**0**	**1**
Undetermined Rodents					
Maxilla	-	1(l)(i)1(r)(i);	-	-	2
Mandible	-	1(l)(i);	2(l)(i);	-	3
I I	-	8(c);	-	1(c);	9
Femur	-	-	1(l)(c);	1(r)(c);	2
Total	**0**	**11**	**3**	**2**	**16**
Grand Total	**11**	**233**	**44**	**13**	**301**

Table 25
Inventory of Rodentia remains, representation of their skeletal elements, and their distribution along the
sequence.
c= complete; i= incomplete; l= left; r= right; p= proximal; d=distal.

Psammomys obesus	N E T I V		H A G	D U D	D					
	Min.	Max.	x	∂	Var.	v	Std.Error	n	95% Lower	95% Upper
Elements										
Length of M $\overline{1}$	1.89	3.32	2.806	0.388	0.151	13.833	0.085	21	2.629	2.983
Width of M $\overline{1}$	1.21	2.10	1.804	0.219	0.048	12.132	0.048	21	1.705	1.904
Length of M $\overline{2}$	1.48	2.28	1.758	0.055	0.055	13.394	0.055	18	1.641	1.875
Width of M $\overline{2}$	1.48	2.21	1.926	0.220	0.048	11.411	0.052	18	1.817	2.035
Length of M $\underline{1}$	2.48	2.76	2.623	0.101	0.010	3.847	0.041	6	2.517	2.729
Width of M $\underline{1}$	1.42	1.91	1.708	0.189	0.036	11.035	0.077	6	1.510	1.906
Length of M $\underline{2}$	1.22	1.74	1.436	0.193	0.037	13.473	0.087	5	1.196	1.676
Width of M $\underline{2}$	1.53	2.52	1.890	0.390	0.152	20.654	0.174	5	1.405	2.375
Length of Lower Alveolar Row	5.45	8.59	7.543	0.796	0.634	10.557	0.188	18	7.147	7.939
Length of Upper Alveolar Row	5.01	8.07	6.322	1.109	1.231	17.549	0.4960	5	4.944	7.700
Elements				R E	C E	N	T			
Length of M $\overline{1}$	1.89	3.54	2.888	0.326	0.106	11.284	0.099	55	2.802	2.975
Width of M $\overline{1}$	1.21	2.25	1.831	0.209	0.044	11.424	0.028	56	1.775	1.887
Length of M $\overline{2}$	1.24	2.43	1.684	0.322	0.104	19.123	0.054	35	1.573	1.795
Width of M $\overline{2}$	1.25	2.31	1.787	0.275	0.075	15.379	0.038	53	1.711	1.862
Length of M $\underline{1}$	2.29	3.90	2.881	0.375	0.141	13.019	0.059	41	2.763	3.000
Width of M $\underline{1}$	1.42	2.24	1.912	0.207	0.043	10.824	0.032	42	1.848	1.977
Length of M $\underline{2}$	1.22	2.08	1.658	0.227	0.051	13.687	0.035	41	1.586	1.729
Width of M $\underline{2}$	1.31	2.63	1.818	0.283	0.080	15.589	0.045	40	1.727	1.908
Length of Lower Alveolar Row	4.53	6.76	5.707	0.573	0.328	10.041	0.097	35	5.511	5.904
Length of Upper Alveolar Row	5.01	8.15	7.077	0.727	0.528	10.272	0.114	41	6.848	7.307

Table 26

Measurements (in mm) of tooth and mandibular elements of *Psammomys obesus* (Rodentia, Gerbillidae) compared with the recent form.

n = number of specimens studied, x = mean, ∂ = Standard deviation, v = coefficient of variation, min = minimum value.

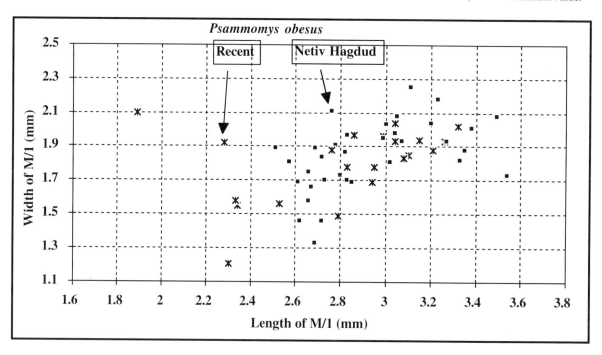

Figure 12

Plot of two variables (width and length) of M1 comparing *Psammomys obesus* from Netiv Hagdud with a few individuals from the Jerusalem region. Although the PPNA assemblage seems to exceed in size the recent sample, two sided *t*-test shows no differences differences between them.

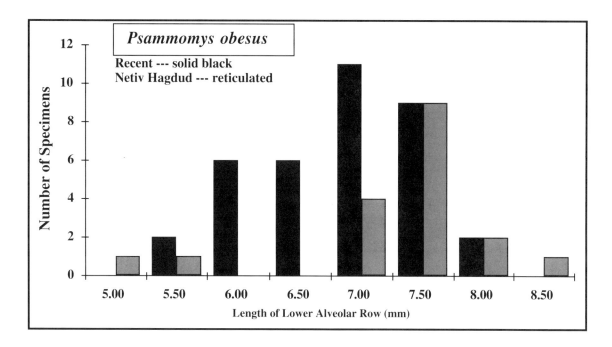

Figure 13
Histogram of measurements of the length of lower alveolar row, comparing the recent and Neolithic assemblages of *Psammomys obesus*. The wide range of variability of the PPNA population may be explained by the larger period of deposition, accumulating more variants with time. The greater size of the molar row of the fossil population is not significant (two-sided *t*-test, see more details in text).

absent from the whole region; the nearest place it can be found today is around Jerusalem.

Spalacidae

Spalax ehrenbergi Nehring, 1898
Within the genus *Spalax* this species delineates the southernmost range; it occurs in the eastern parts of North Africa, but at present the North African and the eastern Mediterranean populations are isolated (Tchernov 1981). The species is known from the Lower Pleistocene in the 'Ubeidiya Formation, and probably underwent autochthonous speciation into several chromosomal groups (Nevo et al. 1988) in this region. Much like *Meriones tristrami,* the lesser mole rat occupies open Mediterranean habitats and is usually not found below the 150 mm isohyet.

The frequency of its occurrence is also similar to *Meriones* (table 25). As an animal highly specialized for subterranean life, this species only rarely falls prey to predators, and its frequency, both in regurgitated pellets of owls and in prehistoric deposits, rarely exceeds 5 percent. It is interesting that in Netiv Hagdud its frequency is conspicuously higher, probably

reflecting its ecological predominance around the site during the PPNA. Today this species is absent from the whole region and its nearest location is the outskirts of Jerusalem.

Muridae

Mus musculus Linnaeus, 1758
The existence of a commensal house mouse in Netiv Hagdud is of great importance as an indication of a long-term human habitation of this site. Therefore we find it necessary to introduce the problem of commensalism and sedentism at some length. Some more general discussion is given in Auffray et al. (1988) and Tchernov (1984, 1991a).

The genus *Mus* originated in the region of Pakistan (Jacobs and Pilbeam 1980), from where four species of mice colonized Eurasia and Africa and in particular the circum-Mediterranean area. One of this species is a human commensal, while the other three are not. Ranck (1968) has generally confirmed Schwartz and Schwartz's (1943) idea of biological segregation in the house mouse of Libya. He pointed out that the dark-bellied specimens from the coastal plain clearly

Meriones tristrami	N E T I V H A G D U D									
	Min.	Max.	x	∂	Var.	v	Std.Error	n	95% Lower	95% Upper
Elements										
Foramen Mandibulare - Symphysis	-	-	11.690	-	-	-	-	1	-	-
Length of Lower Molar Row	-	-	4.560	-	-	-	-	1	-	-
Length of Lower Alveolar Row	5.32	6.75	6.190	0.674	0.583	12.338	0.441	3	4.293	8.087
Length of M $\top$	2.19	2.41	2.285	0.081	0.007	3.555	0.029	8	2.217	2.353
Width of M $\top$	1.41	1.58	1.489	0.064	0.004	4.270	0.022	8	1.436	1.542
Length of M $\overline{2}$	1.26	1.45	1.357	0.092	0.008	6.762	0.046	4	1.211	1.504
Width of M $\overline{2}$	1.47	1.63	1.555	0.066	0.004	4.250	0.033	4	1.450	1.660
Length of M $\overline{3}$	-	-	0.760	-	-	-	-	1	-	-
Width of M $\overline{3}$	-	-	1.120	-	-	-	-	1	-	-
Length of Upper Molar Row	-	-	4.430	-	-	-	-	1	-	-
Length of Upper Alveolar Row	5.49	5.92	5.663	0.227	0.051	4.005	0.131	3	5.100	6.227
Length of M ^{1}	2.45	2.63	2.54	0.127	0.016	5.011	0.090	2	1.396	3.684
Width of M ^{1}	1.18	1.47	1.325	0.205	0.042	15.476	0.145	2	0.517	3.167
Length of M ^{2}	-	-	1.310	-	-	-	-	1	-	-
Width of M ^{2}	-	-	1.310	-	-	-	-	1	-	-
Length of M ^{3}	-	-	0.640	-	-	-	-	1	-	-
Width of M ^{3}	-	-	0.930	-	-	-	-	1	-	-
Spalax ehrenbergi	N E T I V H A G D U D									
Foramen Mentale - Condylus	17.5	19.15	18.325	1.167	1.361	6.367	0.825	2	7.842	28.808
Length of Lower Molar Row	6.22	7.00	6.666	0.317	0.100	4.752	0.142	5	6.273	7.059
Length of Lower Alveolar Row	6.75	7.74	7.288	0.329	0.108	4.513	0.110	9	7.035	7.541
Length of M $\top$	2.36	2.77	2.561	0.156	0.024	6.104	0.059	7	2.417	2.706
Width of M $\top$	1.95	3.31	2.284	0.463	0.214	20.269	0.175	7	1.856	2.713
Length of M $\overline{2}$	1.90	2.61	2.29	0.279	0.078	12.175	0.105	7	2.032	2.548
Width of M $\overline{2}$	1.78	2.33	2.159	0.198	0.039	9.166	0.075	7	1.976	2.342
Length of M $\overline{3}$	1.71	2.06	1.938	0.136	0.018	7.013	0.013	5	1.769	2.107
Width of M $\overline{3}$	1.68	2.10	1.942	0.180	0.032	9.257	0.080	5	1.719	2.165

Table 27

Measurements (in mm) of tooth and jaw elements of *Meriones tristrami* and *Spalax ehrengergi* (Rodentia). n = number of specimens studied, x = mean, ∂ = Standard deviation, v = coefficient of variation, min = minimum value observed, max = maximum value observed, 95% lower = 95% confidence interval of the mean, 95% upper = 95% confidence interval of the mean.

represent the commensal form, *Mus musculus brevirostris*, which (like many other domesticated and commensal forms) possesses a shorter rostrum compared with wild or feral forms in other localities. He could not confirm, however, the coexistence of a long-tailed type along the Libyan coast. Ranck (1968) also found different color types in different localities and interpreted these as various stages of commensalism rather than a distinct subspecies. Setzer (1957) also maintained that *Mus musculus* has been segregated in Libya into commensal and wild/feral types, although they were not as distinguishable as Schwartz and Schwartz (1943) have shown. Osborn and Helmy (1980: 281) indicated that the Nile and Delta populations are slightly smaller on average than those from other parts of Egypt. They explained the relative uni-

formity of the Egyptian populations by the continuous transportation of house mice "up and down the Nile Valley and delta and between the Nile and the Suez Canal zone and the more accessible oases for a long period of time." Behavioral segregation between wild/feral and commensal types was also claimed to occur. Osborn and Helmy (1980) have stated that commensal populations tend to be less nocturnal than the wild types.

Fossil mice have occurred in Southeast Asia from early Pleistocene to historical times, which enabled us to closely follow almost the entire Quaternary period (Tchernov 1968, 1986). Recently, two species of mice were described from the Israeli fauna: the commensal house mouse (*Mus musculus domesticus*) and a wild-range mouse (*Mus macedonicus* or "*Mus spretoides*," Auffray et al. 1988, 1990). The fossil record shows that the two extant species have coexisted as two different lineages ever since the Natufian period. *Mus musculus domesticus* occurs all over the southern Levant while *Mus macedonicus* ("*Mus spretoides*") occurs along the western coastal plain of the eastern Mediterranean and on the hills and mountains of northern Israel. Therefore it seems that humidity plays an important role in the repartition of the wild *Mus macedonicus*, as it has essentially adapted itself to a Mediterranean climate. Indeed, the boundaries of both species are well correlated with the annual 400 mm isohyet that generally delimits the Mediterranean climatic belt. *Mus macedonicus* has been trapped principally in two different environments: sand dune beaches and bushes up to an altitude of 500 m (especially associated with *Pistacia lentiscus*). Very rarely has this species been trapped in natural habitats or agricultural fields.

The association of the recent material with one of the two species is determined by a powerful discriminative index: head and body length/length of the tail. The RDI parameter (*rangeé dentaire inferieure* or length of the lower tooth row, Auffray et al. 1988, 1990) is classically treated by comparing the mean and the range of variation for all the fossil and the recent assemblages. However, skull and mandible parameters were found to be specifically characteristic and enabled a good discrimination between *Mus musculus domesticus* and *Mus macedonicus* (Auffray et al. 1988, 1990). These features have been established for the recent species (Orsini et al. 1983) and have been applied by us to the fossil assemblages that have been derived from 13 prehistoric levels throughout the Late, Middle, and Upper Pleistocene. The CZ parameters (width of the anterior part of the malar process/width of the upper part of the zygomatic arch) were treated by a discriminant analysis performed on recent material data, while the fossil data were added as supplementary individuals.

The discriminant analysis performed on CZ provided a definitive discrimination between the recent species of mice. All of the fossil assemblages from Oumm-Qatafa (Late Acheulian) to Hayonim C (Kebaran), ranging from Middle Pleistocene to Epipaleolithic, were classified as *Mus macedonicus*. In Hayonim Cave level B (Natufian) both wild species of *Mus* as well as *Mus musculus domesticus* were found. The RDI of the two extant species in the southern Levant, *Mus musculus domesticus* and *Mus macedonicus* were compared with all the thirteen above mentioned

assemblages. Thus, *Mus musculus* appears for the first time in level B of Hayonim Cave as a new species (for more details see Auffray et al. 1988, 1990). These Natufian populations are the earliest known house mice, and may have speciated in situ during this relatively extremely short period. We have to be aware of the unique anthropogenic habitat that was essentially isolated from the natural ecosystem and may be ecologically regarded as a small island where morphogenetical changes may occur very rapidly. *Mus musculus* is, therefore, a newly created species, with unique morphological and behavioral characteristics, that is essentially commensal and mainly associated with human habitations.

The house mouse is the second most common rodent at Netiv Hagdud of which 61 items were found (table 25). Mandibles and M1 were the most frequent elements in the assemblage. A comparison of the lower and upper molars is given in table 28. The significant differences between the wild species *Mus macedonicus* (*Mus "spretoides"*) and both the recent populations of *Mus musculus* and the *Mus* assemblage from Netiv Hagdud become obvious especially when comparing the sizes and proportions of M1. Two-tailed "*t*" values for these samples have shown that for a 5 percent level of significance *Mus macedonicus* and *Mus musculus* (both the recent and the fossil populations from Netiv Hagdud) are highly separated (p=0.0001); in contrast, between the recent and the fossil *Mus musculus*, values are around p=0.5, remaining in agreement with Auffray's et al. (1988) results. The differences between the wild and the commensal species are demonstrated in figures 14, 15, and 16. In each case *Mus musculus* concentrates around the lowermost levels of *Mus macedonicus*, and falls within the size and proportion of the female and/or young group of *Mus macedonicus*.

Mus musculus, as an obligatory commensal species, was common in the settlement of Netiv Hagdud and evidently shows a long-term occupation of the site. A more detailed discussion of this issue will be given in the last chapter.

Arvicolidae

Arvicola terrestris (Linnaeus, 1758)

The water vole is widely distributed in Eurasia but at present is not found anywhere south of Turkey along the eastern Mediterranean coast, although it still occurs in Mesopotamia. The last record of this species from the southern Levant goes back to 1940–1950

Mus musculus domesticus	N E T I V H A G D U D									
	Min.	Max.	x	∂	Var.	v	Std.Error	n	95% Lower	95% Upper
Elements										
Length of M_1	1.48	1.59	1.541	0.041	0.0020	2.645	0.014	9	1.510	1.572
Width of M_1	0.91	0.96	0.934	0.018	0.0003	1.937	0.006	9	0.921	0.948
Length of M^1	1.60	1.90	1.768	0.125	0.0160	7.058	0.008	5	1.613	1.923
Width of M^1	1.14	1.20	1.166	0.023	0.0010	1.974	0.010	5	1.137	1.195
Mus musculus domesticus	R E C E N T									
Length of M_1	1.34	1.59	1.468	0.009	0.0040	4.178	0.009	42	1.449	1.487
Width of M_1	0.78	0.99	0.903	0.045	0.0020	4.931	0.007	42	0.889	0.917
Length of M^1	1.34	1.59	1.468	0.061	0.0040	4.178	0.009	42	1.449	1.487
Width of M^1	0.78	0.99	0.903	0.045	0.0020	4.931	0.007	42	0.889	0.917
Mus macedonicus	Q A F Z E H									
Length of M_1	1.40	2.20	1.606	0.178	0.0320	11.076	0.010	332	1.587	1.625
Width of M_1	0.85	1.40	1.002	0.099	0.0100	9.875	0.005	332	0.991	1.012
Length of M^1	1.55	2.35	1.817	0.168	0.0280	9.254	0.014	145	1.790	1.845
Width of M^1	1.00	1.55	1.155	0.095	0.0090	8.189	0.008	145	1.140	1.171

Table 28

Measurements (in mm) of lower and upper first molars of recent and fossil *Mus musculus* (from Netiv Hagdud) compared with the "wild" species *Mus macedonicus* from the Mousterian deposits of Qafzeh Cave (Galilee, Israel).
n = number of specimens studied, x = mean, ∂ = Standard deviation, v = coefficient of variation, min = minimum value observed, max = maximum value observed, 95% lower = 95% confidence interval of the mean, 95% upper = 95% confidence interval of the mean.

when it was recorded from owl pellets only (Dor 1947). This aquatic vole is found in the vicinity of different water bodies and displays many specialized traits for aquatic life: swimming, diving, and digging deep burrows along water banks.

The fossil record of Netiv Hagdud is confined to four specimens (table 25), which together with the record we have from the site of Gilgal, indicates the existence of an extensive body of freshwater body in the vicinity of the site. Common predators which could have inconspicuously deposited these remains in the site were owls and cats. A wild cat (see below) was indeed found in the record of both Gilgal and Netiv Hagdud.

Microtus guentheri (Danford and Alston, 1880)
This species is often included within the widely distributed *Microtus socialis* (Harrison 1972). Due to its long geographic isolation from northern populations of *Microtus socialis* by the Taurus and the Zagros and Lebanon mountain chains, we prefer to specifically separate the southern Levantine form, *Microtus guentheri*, from the northern one.

This highly colonial vole favors mesic terrain covered with grass, but may extend its distribution also to bushy scrub land. This species will rarely cross the boundary of 350 isohyet. The record of this species, even if it is confined to one specimen, clearly indicates profound habitat changes since the PPNA.

Lagomorpha

Leporidae
Lepus capensis Linnaeus, 1758
The extremely wide distribution of the Cape hare indicates its versatility in adapting to a wide spectrum of habitats, climatic zones, and landscapes. The hare is a totally vegetarian species and may digest a rich diversity of plants, from grasses to aromatic and alkaloidal leaves like *Artemisia*, *Salvia*, and various bulbs, such as *Eremerus* or *Tulipa*. In the southern Levantine province the distribution of *Lepus* indeed covers almost all possible landscapes and all climatic belts.

Hares became more abundant in the human diet in the Upper Paleolithic, particularly emerging as a significant source of protein during the Epipaleolithic. Hare remains are relatively common (table 29), and in at least one case there is a direct indication of their having been used for food: a radius from the Upper Area (table 29) displays fine cut marks. The fact that relatively more bone remains were retrieved from the Upper Area, where as a rule there is a poorer representation of small- and medium-sized animals, suggests that the deposition of hares was essentially anthropogenic. Other consumers of hares are mainly

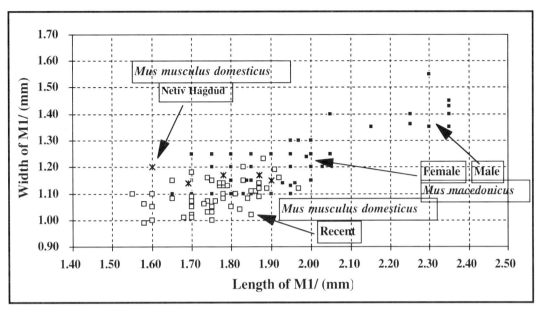

Figure 14
A scatter diagram comparing two variables (width and length) of M1 of males and females of the wild mouse (*Mus macedonicus*) from the Mousterian level of Qafzeh Cave (Galilee, Israel) with two assemblages of the commensal house mouse (*Mus musculus*) from Netiv Hagdud and recent specimens from the Mediterranean region of Israel. In each case *Mus musculus* concentrates around the lower range (within the female range) of *Mus macedonicus*. These variables are somewhat larger in the PPNA population of Mus musculus compared with the recent one. No sexual dimorphism is shown in the house mouse.

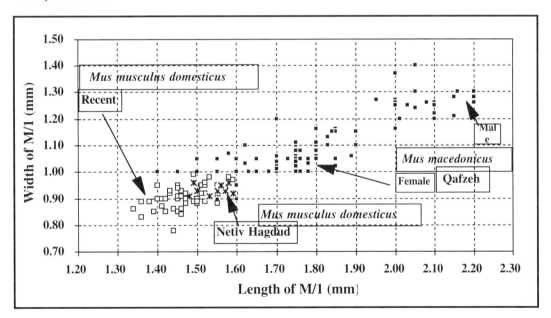

Figure 15
Plot of two variables (width and length) of M1 of males and females of the wild mouse (*Mus macedonicus*) from the Mousterian level of Qafzeh Cave (Galilee, Israel) with two assemblages of the commensal house mouse (*Mus musculus*) from Netiv Hagdud and of recent specimens from the Mediterranean region of Israel. In each case *Mus musculus* concetrates around the lower range (within the female range) of *Mus macedonicus*. These variables are somewhat larger in the PPNA population of *Mus musculus* compared with the recent one. No sexual dimorphism is shown in the house mouse, but dimorphism is sharply defined in the wild mouse.

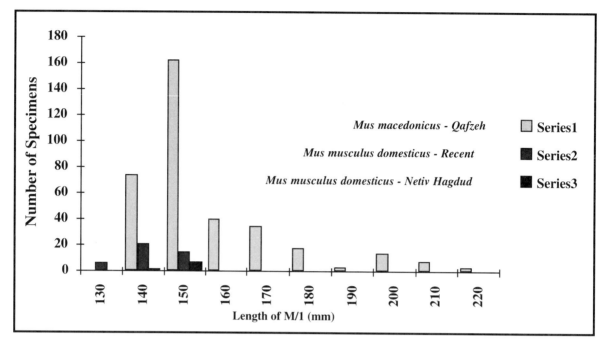

Figure 16
Histogram of measurements of the length of M1 of the wild mouse (*Mus macedonicus*) from the Mousterian level of Qafzeh Cave (Galilee, Israel) with two assemblages of the commensal house mouse (*Mus musculus*) from Netiv Hagdud and of recent specimens from the Mediterranean region of Israel. In each case *Mus musculus* concentrates around the lower range (within the female range) of *Mus macedonicus*. These variables are somewhat larger in the PPNA population of *Mus musculus* compared with the recent one. No sexual dimorphism is shown in the house mouse, but dimorphism is very conspicuous in the wild mouse.

large eagles (like *Aquila chrysætos*) or foxes (like *Vulpes vulpes*) that normally avoid direct interaction with humans.

The abundance of skeletal parts, as represented in table 30 and in figure 17, does not show preferences for special body parts, all of which have been evenly deposited. The higher representation of the metatarsals is due to the combining all metatarsals into one category.

Carnivora

The species diversity and the quantity of carnivore remains from Netiv Hagdud is relatively small and may indicate high and intensive year-round activity around and within the site. Most carnivores avoid direct confrontation with humans. Therefore most of the species will be excluded not only from the settlement itself but also from its surrounding areas. Indeed, from Netiv Hagdud there is only one abundant carnivore species, the fox, a typically synan-

thropic animal. The rest of the carnivore faunal record is comprised of a few dog and wild cat remains.

Canidae
Vulpes vulpes (Linnaeus, 1758)
Much as with *Lepus capensis*, the red fox is widespread over large geographical regions across the Palearctic realm, is extremely variable in morphology, and is highly euryoecious, covering almost all possible climatic belts and landscapes. It is only in some special habitats, restricted to relatively small geographical regions, that it may be excluded by more specialized species like the sand fox (*Vulpes rüppelli*) or the Blandford's fox (*Vulpes cana*) (Dayan et al. 1989).

One hundred fifty-two red fox bones were uncovered from the site (table 31) thus making it one of the most abundant medium- to large-sized mammals in the fossil record. No special selection of skeletal elements has been found for this species; most are more or less evenly represented, although vertebrae are rather rare (fig. 17). The somewhat higher represen-

AREA		DEEP SOUNDING			UPPER AREA	Total
Element	Complex	Lower Complex	Middle Complex	Upper Complex		
Lepus capensis						
Basioccipitale		----------------	1(c);	----------------	----------------------	1
Upper Jaw		2(?)(p);	1(r)(c); 1(r)(p);	----------------	----------------------	4
Mandible		----------------	2(l+r)(p);	2(r+l)(p); 1(l)(c);	2(r+l)(p);	7
Molars + Premolars (isolated)		3(?)(c);	3(c);	----------------	----------------------	6
Scapula		----------------	1(l)(p);	2(r+l)(c);	1(l)(p);	4
Humerus		----------------	2(l+r)(p); 2(l)(d);	2(r+l)(d);	1(r)(d);	7
Radius		----------------	1(r)(p); 2(r+l)(p); 1(?)(p);	----------------	*1 (?)(p);	5
Ulna		1(r)(p);	2(r+l)(p);	1(r)(p);	----------------------	4
Calcaneum		----------------	2(r)(c);	1(l)(c);	1(r)(c);	4
Astragalus		----------------	1(r)(c);	----------------	----------------------	1
Metacarpus III		----------------	4(?)(c);	----------------	2(?)(?); 1(r)(?);	7
Pelvis		----------------	--------------------------	1(?);	2(r)(d); 2(?);	5
Femur		----------------	--------------------------	1(r)(p);	1(l)(d); 1(r)(p);	3
Tibia		----------------	1(r)(d); 3(l+2r)(p);	----------------	2(r)(d);	6
Metatarsus III		1(?)(d);	2(r+l)(c); 1(?)(d);	1(?)(c);	2(?)(d);1(?)(p);2(?)(c);	10
Metatarsus IV		2(?)(d);	1(?)(d);	----------------	2(?)(d+p); 1 (r)(c);	6
Phalanx 1, digit III			1(r)(c);	----------------	----------------------	1
Metapodium (non-diagnostic)		2(?)(i);	--------------------------	----------------	1(?)(?);	3
Total		11	35	12	26	84

Table 29
Inventory of undetermined *Lepus capensis* remains, representation of their skeletal elements and their distribution along the sequence.
c= complete; i= incomplete; l= left; r= right; p= proximal; d=distal; ?= side unknown; *=cut marks.

Skeletal Elements	*Lepus capensis*	*Vulpes vulpes*	*Canis familiaris*	*Felis* spp.
Basioccipitale	1 (1.2%)	0	0	0
Mandible	7 (8.4%)	20 (13.8%)	0	4 (26.7%)
Isolated teeth	6 (7.2%)	38 (26.0%)	0	1 (6.6%)
Upper jaw	4 (4.8%)	6 (4.2%)	0	0
Scapula	4 (4.8%)	3 (2.1%)	0	0
Humerus	7 (8.4%)	6 (4.2%)	0	1 (6.6%)
Radius	5 (6.0%)	12 (8.4%)	0	2 (13.4%)
Ulna	4 (4.8%)	4 (2.8%)	0	0
Metacarpus II-III	7 (8.4%)	4 (2.8%)	0	1 (6.6%)
Pelvis	5 (6.0%)	4 (2.8%)	0	0
Femur	3 (3.6%)	9 (6.2%)	1 (50%)	0
Tibia	6 (7.2%)	8 (5.4%)	0	0
Metatarsus II-IV	16 (19.1%)	2 (1.4%)	0	0
Phalanxes	1 (1.2%)	18 (12.4%)	1 (50%)	5 (33.3%)
Metapodials (non-diagnostic)	3 (3.6%)	10 (6.8%)	0	1 (6.6%)
Vertebrae	0	2 (1.4%)	0	0
Total	79	146	2	15
				Grand Total: 242
M.N.I.	**5** (=number of pelves)	**6** (=12/2 radii)	**1**	**2** (= 4/2 mand.) **Total: 14**

Table 30
Number of skeletal elements and their percentage representation in lagomorphs and carnivores, and the minimum number of individuals (MNI) per skeletal parts.

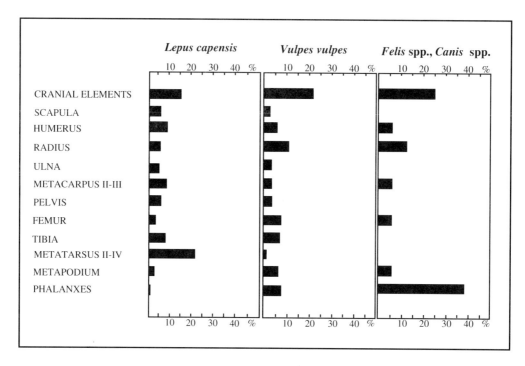

Figure 17
Relative representation of the skeletal parts of *Lepus capensis*, *Vulpes vulpes*, and *Felis* spp. + *Canis* spp. from the PPNA of Netiv Hagdud. There is some preference for metatarsals in hares, but high selection for phalanxes in *Felis* + *Canis* which were probably used as tools and/or ornaments. No preferences are shown for foxes.

tation of cranial elements may be a result of the cultural use of canine teeth, a phenomenon that is well known from all Natufian sites. The high frequency of fox remains may reflect this animal's great abundance and long-term activities around the site, probably taking advantage of food refuse in the modified anthropogenic habitat, lower diversity of species, and concomitant lower competition for anthropogenic food resources (Tchernov 1984). The fox may be considered, as we know from its present behavior around human settlements, a synanthropic species that efficiently exploits human resources with almost no harm to the local inhabitants.

Canis familiaris Linnaeus, 1758
A few remains of dog were retrieved among the carnivore material (tables 31, 32). Dog remains are rarely found in the Natufian and Neolithic sites, which prevents thorough quantitative comparisons of these early Middle Eastern forms of domesticated wolves. The Netiv Hagdud specimens seem to fall within the sizes of the Natufian dogs as described by Davis and Valla (1978) and Dayan et al. (1989).

Clutton-Brock argues that at Jericho two mandibles were identified as *Canis*, where the premolar teeth were "so crowded and displaced that they probably belonged to tamed wolves, if not to domesticated dogs" (1979:141). Further on she pointed out that "the specimen that looks most like dog is the earliest, that is the burnt mandibular ramus from the proto-Neolithic (ca. 10,500 B.P.)" (ibid.). The earliest well-established evidence for the presence of domesticated dogs is known from the Natufian period (Davis and Valla 1978).

Felidae
Felis silvestris Schreber, 1777
This essentially European, eastern Mediterranean species usually occupies woodland areas. Cats as a rule are extremely rare in the fossil record of prehistoric human occupations. Therefore the retrieval of 14 skeletal elements (tables 31, 32), small a number that it is, suggests a relative abundance of wild cat in the area. As a species that is well adapted to living in

AREA	DEEP SOUNDING			UPPER AREA	Total
Element | Complex	Lower Complex	Middle Complex	Upper Complex		
Vulpes vulpes					
Mandible	2(r+l)(i); 1(l)(+P$_4$,M$_2$,M$_4$); 1(r)(+P3-4,M1-2);	5(3r+2l)(i); 1(r)(+M$_{1-2}$);2(l)(+P$_{2-4}$);1(r)(+M$_{1-2}$);1(r)(P$_{1-3}$);	1(l)(+P$_3$,M$_2$);1(l)(+P$_4$,M$_{1-2}$);2(r)(i);	2(l)(i);	20
C$_1$	----------------------	1(r)(i); 1(r)(c);	1(l)(i);	----------------------	3
M$_1$	1(i);	4(2r+2l)(c);	1(l)(c); 1(l)(i);	----------------------	7
M$_2$	----------------------	2(r+l)(c);	----------------------	----------------------	2
P$_2$	----------------------	1(r)(c);	1(?)(i);	----------------------	2
P$_3$	1(r);	1(r)(c);	----------------------	----------------------	2
P$_4$	----------------------	1(r)(i); 2(r)(c);	1(?)(i);	----------------------	4
Upper Jaw	----------------------	2(r+l)(i); 2(r)(+P$_4$,M$_2$); 1(l)(+P$_4$,M$_{1-2}$);	1(r)(i);	----------------------	6
P$_2$	----------------------	2(r+l)(c);	----------------------	----------------------	2
P$_4$	----------------------	2(r+l)(i); 3(r)(c);	----------------------	----------------------	5
M$_1$	1(l)(i);	4(3r+l)(c);	----------------------	1(r)(i); 1(l)(+C,P$_{2dec}$);	7
M$_2$	----------------------	1(r)(i); 1(r)(c);	----------------------	1(r)(i);	4
Scapula	----------------------	1(r)(glenoid);	1(l)(glenoid);	1(r)(c);	3
Humerus	----------------------	2(2r+2l)(d);	1(r)(d); 1(l)(p);	----------------------	6
Radius	1(r)(p);	6(3r+3l)(d); 2(r+l)(p);	2(l)(p);	1(l)(p);	12
Ulna	----------------------	1(l)(p);	----------------------	3(2r+l)(p);	4
Metacarpus II-III	1(?)(c);	2(?)(c);	----------------------	1(?)(c);	4
Femur	1(l)(p);	1(l)(d);3(l)(p);	2(r)(d);	1(r)(p); 1(r)(d);	9
Tibia	----------------------	1(r)(p);1(l)(d);	1(l)(p); 1(r)(c);	1(l)(p); 3(r)(d);	8
Calcaneum	1(r)(c);	4(2r+2l)(c);	2(?)(d) ;2(?)(p);	----------------------	6
Metatarsus II	----------------------	--------------------------------	1(?)(c);	1(?)(i);	1
Metatarsus III	----------------------	1(?)(d);	----------------------	----------------------	1
Pelvis (acetabulum)	----------------------	1(l)(i);	----------------------	1(l)(i);	4
Metapodium (non-diagnostic)	----------------------	2(?)(c);2(?)(p);	----------------------	2(?)(d); 1(?)(d);	10
Phalanx 1	----------------------	13(?)(c);1(?)(p);	----------------------	2(?)(c);	17
Phalanx 3	----------------------	1(?)(c);	----------------------	----------------------	1
Atlas	----------------------	--------------------------------	----------------------	1(c);	1
Axis	----------------------	--------------------------------	1(p);	----------------------	1
Total	11	89	28	24	**152**

Table 31

Inventory of *Vulpes vulpes* remains, representation of their skeletal elements, and their distribution along the sequence.
c= complete; i= incomplete; l= left; r= right; p= proximal; d=distal; ?= side unknown.

AREA	DEEP SOUNDING			UPPER AREA	Total
Element | Complex	Lower Complex	Middle Complex	Upper Complex		
Felis silvestris					
Mandible	----------------------	1(r)(+P$_{3dec}$,M$_1$);1(l)(+P$_{3dec}$,M$_1$);	----------------	1(l)(+M13); 1(r)(i);	4
P$_4$	----------------------	1(l)(c);	----------------	------------------	1
Radius	----------------------	--------------------------------	1(l)(p);	1(r)(p);	2
Metacarpus III	----------------------	--------------------------------	1(?)(c);	------------------	1
Metatarsus II	----------------------	1(?)(c);	----------------	------------------	1
Phalanx 1	----------------------	2(?)(c);	1(?)(c);	------------------	3
Phalanx 2	----------------------	1(?)(c);	----------------	------------------	1
Metapodium (non-diagnostic)	----------------------	1(?)(p);	----------------	------------------	1
Total	**0**	**8**	**3**	**3**	**14**
Caracal caracal					
Humerus	----------------------	1(r)(d);	----------------	------------------	1
Phalanx 1	----------------------	1(?)(c);	----------------	------------------	1
Total		2		0	**2**
Canis cf. familiaris					
Femur	----------------------	1(r)(p);	1(r)(p);	------------------	2
Phalanx 1	----------------------	1(?)(c);	----------------	------------------	1
Total	**0**	**2**	**1**	**0**	**3**
Grand Total	**0**	**12**	**4**	**3**	**19**

Table 32

Inventory of *Felis* and *Canis* remains, representation of their skeletal elements, and their distribution along the sequence.
c= complete; i= incomplete; l= left; r= right; p= proximal; d=distal; ?= side unknown.

forests and woods, its common record from Netiv Hagdud implies again that a wooded region existed in the vicinity of the site. At present this species is rare in the southern Levant.

Caracal caracal (Schreber, 1776)

The caracal cat is of an Afro-tropical origin and populates the southern Levantine, Mesopotamian, and Indian regions only sparsely. It is usually associated with arid, semiarid, and subtropical scrub forest, preferring hilly country characterized by scattered sparse vegetation. In some places along the Syro-African Rift the caracal prefers tropical thorn forest and savanna landscapes. At present it has a very patchy distribution due to extensive hunting in the recent past.

The recent distribution of caracals in the arid zones of southwest Asia may have been largely configured by anthropogenic factors. The caracal is not only highly tolerant of human disturbance, but in many places, where hunting pressure is low, it tends to be attracted to human habitations and makes use of the relatively higher distribution of other commensal and small domesticated species, especially rodents, dogs, and cats.

The faunal record is confined to two bones (table 32), sufficient to indicate the coexistence of at least two different species of cats in the highly variegated and rich habitats in the Lower Jordan Valley.

Figure 17 shows the representation of the skeletal elements of *Canis* and *Felis*. The higher number of phalanxes may be due to the usefulness of the sharp claws, as with the raptors. A comparison of the frequency of skeletal elements of Leporidae, Carnivora and Artiodactyla is given in figure 18, showing that the principal differences are recognized in the metapodials and phalanxes.

Artiodactyla

When compared with other contemporaneous sites in more mesic regions of the Levant, artiodactyl species diversity is relatively low. In most PPNA sites that are

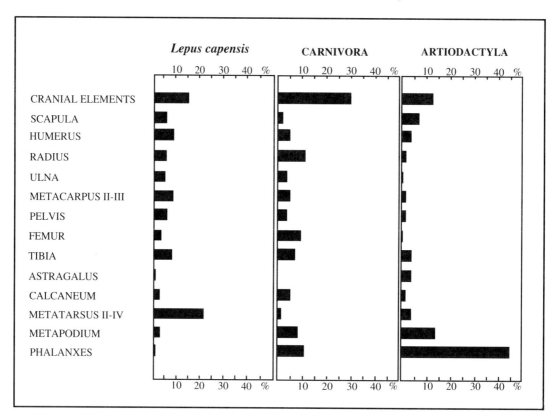

Figure 18
Relative representation of skeletal parts of *Lepus capensis*, with carnivores and artiodactyls from the PPNA of Netiv Hagdud. There is an obvious preference for phalanxes in the artiodactyls (see text for more details), but low preferences for specific elements in carnivores taken as a whole.

situated in the Mediterranean belt, three sympatric species of Cervidae coexisted: *Capreolus capreolus, Cervus elaphus,* and *Dama mesopotamica*. In Netiv Hagdud only *Dama mesopotamica* is recorded. The absence of *Bos primigenius* from Netiv Hagdud, the scarcity of *Dama*, and the absence of the two other species of deer indicate that as mesic as this region was during the PPNA period, the local ecosystem could hardly support all these typical woodland Mediterranean species. Yet it is worthwhile to mention that in the nearby site of Gilgal, of a somewhat earlier period than Netiv Hagdud, one astragalum of *Bos primigenius* was identified (Noy et al. 1980). Both *Bos primigenius* and *Capreolus capreolus* were mentioned in the PPNA of Jericho, some 13 km south of Netiv Hagdud, where

the more luxurious habitat could have supported a higher diversity of herbivores.

The paucity of artiodactyl material, except *Gazella gazella* which is also not very abundant, did not allow us to conduct quantitative comparative analysis. The distribution of elements of all the artiodactyl species in this site is given in table 33. Evidently, large mammals were not heavily exploited, and their relative contribution to the subsistence of the local inhabitants was not significant.

Bovidae
Gazella gazella (Pallas, 1776)

Although the mountain gazelle constitutes a dominant component of the artiodactyl assemblage, its fre-

AREA	DEEP SOUNDING			UPPER AREA	Total
Element　｜　Complex	Lower Complex	Middle Complex	Upper Complex		
Gazella gazella					
Horn cores	-------------------	1(l)(c)(m); 3(?)(i)(m);	-------------------	1(?)(i)(m); 5(2l+3r)(c)(m);	10
Mandible	-------------------	1(r)(i); 1(symph.)(i);	-------------------	1(l)(i);	3
M$_1$	-------------------	1(l)(c);	-------------------	-------------------	1
M$_2$	-------------------	1(r)(c);	-------------------	-------------------	1
P$_3$	-------------------	1(l)(c);	-------------------	-------------------	1
Upper Jaw	-------------------	1(r)(i);1(l)(i)(+ M^1-M^3);1(r)(i)(+ P^2)	-------------------	-------------------	3
Scapula	-------------------	2(l)(p); 3(r)(p);	-------------------	1(r)(p); 3(l)(p);	9
Humerus	1(l)(i);	1(r)(d);1(l)(d); 1(l)(p);	-------------------	1(r)(d);	5
Radius	1(l)(d)(j);	1(l)(p);	-------------------	-------------------	2
Ulna	-------------------	1(l)(d);	-------------------	-------------------	1
Metacarpus	-------------------	1(r)(c);	-------------------	1(l)(d);	2
Pelvis	-------------------	1(r)(i);	-------------------	1(r)(i);	2
Femur	-------------------	1(l)(p);	-------------------	-------------------	1
Tibia	-------------------	2(r)(d); 1(l)(d);	-------------------	-------------------	3
Astragalus	1(r)(c)(j);	1(r)(i); 1(r)(c); 2(l)(c);	-------------------	-------------------	5
Calcaneum	-------------------	1(l)(c)(*);	-------------------	-------------------	1
Metatarsus	-------------------	2(r)(c)(*); 1(r)(d); 1(r)(d)(j);	-------------------	-------------------	4
Metapodium (non-diagnostic)	1(r)(d)(j);	7(l)(d); 6(r)(d); 1(?)(shaft)(j);	-------------------	2(l)(d); 1(l)(c);	18
Phalanx 1	-------------------	5(r)(c); 5(l)(c); 1(l)(d)(*);	1(l)(c);	6(l)(c); 5(r)(c); 1(?)(p);	24
Phalanx 2	2(l+r)(c);	4(r)(c); 6(l)(c);	-------------------	1(l+r)(c);	13
Phalanx 3	-------------------	3(r)(c); 3(l)(c);	-------------------	4(l)(c); 2(r)(c);	12
Total	**6**	**78**	**1**	**36**	**121**
Alcelaphus buselaphus					
Phalanx 2	-------------------	-------------------	-------------------	1(l)(c);	1
Total	**0**	**0**	**0**	**1**	**1**
Sus scrofa					
I^2	-------------------	1(?)(c);	-------------------	-------------------	1
I$_2$	1(l)(c);	-------------------	-------------------	-------------------	1
M$_2$	-------------------	-------------------	-------------------	1(?)(i);	1
Phalanx 1	-------------------	1(l)(c);	-------------------	-------------------	1
Phalanx 2	-------------------	1(l)(c);	-------------------	1(r)(c); 1(l)(c);	3
Phalanx 3	-------------------	1(r)(c);	-------------------	-------------------	1
Total	**1**	**4**	**0**	**3**	**8**
Dama mesopotamica					
Tibia	-------------------	1(l)(d);	-------------------	-------------------	1
Total	**0**	**1**	**0**	**0**	**1**
Capra ibex					
M$_3$	-------------------	-------------------	1(r)(c);	-------------------	1
Phalanx 2	1(?)(i);	-------------------	-------------------	-------------------	1
Total	**1**	**0**	**1**	**0**	**2**
Grand Total	**8**	**83**	**2**	**40**	**133**

Table 33
Inventory of artiodactyl remains, representation of their skeletal elements, and their distribution along the sequence.
c= complete; i= incomplete; l= left; r= right; p= proximal; d=distal; ?= side unknown; j=Juvenile; m=male; (*)=burnt.

quencies, when compared to the abundance of gazelle throughout the Natufian sequence, indicate a swift and drastic decrease in exploitation of gazelles during the PPNA. The relative distribution in other PPNA sites in the region (Gilgal, Noy et al. 1980; Jericho, Clutton-Brock 1979) shows roughly the same low frequencies of artiodactyls in general and gazelles in particular. This issue will be further discussed in the last chapter.

As shown in table 33, from the 121 bones recovered, 78 originated in the Middle Complex, 36 in the Upper Area, six were from the Lower Complex, and only one came from the Upper Complex. The number of skeletal elements, their small MNI, and the calculation of the meat weight are given in table 34.

In general the measurements of all the available skeletal elements of Netiv Hagdud population do not show any significant differences from the recent populations of gazelles in Israel (table 35). Apparently few changes took place in the local populations of mountain gazelles during the Holocene. It seems that if any size decrease did occur during the Holocene (as

argued by Davis 1981), it happened some time before the PPNA, probably during the later part of the Natufian. Yet we must take into account that any size decrease found within the Natufian populations was caused by intentional over-culling of males as was recently shown by Cope (1991). Only one variable seems to show some differences from the recent form: as shown in figure 19 the distal end of phalanx 1 of the PPNA population is larger and shorter. As shown in figures 20 and 21, sexual dimorphism for the third phalanx is low in the recent populations of gazelles, but there is a significant difference in the size and morphology of the last phalanx between the recent and Neolithic populations of *Gazella gazella*. The population of Netiv Hagdud shows a reduction (particularly in the width) of the last phalanx, a phenomenon that is quite similar to what was described for the Natufian gazelles (Cope 1991; Horwitz et al. 1991). This is probably a result of the intensive male culling practiced by the PPNA people of Netiv Hagdud. Figure 21 also shows that the last phalanx of the Neolithic population is much shorter and more stout, which

Skeletal Elements	Gazella gazella	Alcelaphus buselaphus	Capra ibex	Sus scrofa	Dama mesopotamica	Artiodactyla Undetermined
Scapula	8 (7.32%)	-	-	1 (5.88%)	-	-
Humerus	5 (4.59%)	-	-	1 (5.88%)	-	-
Radius	2 (1.83%)	-	-	1 (5.88%)	-	-
Ulna	1 (1.42%)	-	-	-	-	-
Astragalus	4 (3.66%)	-	-	1 (5.88%)	-	-
Calcaneum	1 (1.42%)	-	-	-	-	-
Carpale 2+3	3 (2.75%)	-	-	-	-	-
Metacarpus	1 (1.42%)	-	-	-	-	-
Phalanx 1	20 (18.34%)	-	-	1 (5.88%)	-	-
Phalanx 2	10 (9.17%)	1 (100%)	-	3 (17.65%)	-	-
Phalanx 3	9 (8.26%)	-	-	1 (5.88%)	-	-
Pelvis	2 (1.83%)	-	-	-	-	-
Femur	1 (1.42%)	-	-	-	-	-
Tibia	4 (3.66%)	-	-	-	2 (66.66%)	-
Metatarsus	4 (3.66%)	-	-	-	-	-
Metapodium	16 (14.68%)	-	-	-	-	1 (50%)
Maxillary	2 (1.83%)	-	-	2 (11.76%)	1 (33.33%)	1 (50%)
Mandible	2 (1.83%)	-	-	2 (11.76%)	-	-
Isolated Teeth	4 (3.66%)	-	1 (100%)	4 (23.53%)	-	-
Horn Cores	10 (9.17%)	-	-	-	-	-
Total	**109**	**1**	**1**	**17**	**3**	**2**
						Grand Total: 133
M.N.I.	**5**(=10/2 horncores)	**1**	**1**	**2**(=3/2 Phal.2+0.5)	**1** (=2/2 tibia)	**1** **Grand Total: 10**
Total Weight Estimation (kg)*	21x5= **105**	1x80= **80**	1x50=**50**	2x40= **80**	1x55= **55**	1x35=**35** **Grand Total: 405**

Table 34
Number of skeletal elements and their percentage representation in the artiodactyla, and the minimum number of individuals (MNI) per skeletal part. Assuming that each hunted individual reflects a complete carcass consumed in the site.
*Mean weight of *Gazella gazella*: 21kg.
*Mean weight of *Alcelaphus buselaphus*: 80 kg.
*Mean weight of *Capra ibex*: 50 kg.
*Mean weight of *Sus scrofa*: 40 kg.
*Mean weight of *Dama mesopotamica*: 55 kg.

Gazella gazella	N	E	T	I	V	H	A	G	D	U	D	
	Min.	Max.	x	∂	Var.	v	Std.Error	n	95% Lower	95% Upper		
Elements												
Phalanx 1												
Greatest Length	36.17	45.72	39.729	2.826	7.985	7.112	0.685	17	38.276	42.182		
Distal Breadth	7.90	9.66	8.745	0 .443	0.196	5.064	0.107	17	8.517	8.972		
Proximal Breadth	8.78	11.79	10.535	0.210	0.746	8.200	0.21	17	10.091	10.979		
Phalanx 2												
Greatest Length	19.99	24.99	22.425	1.803	3.252	8.042	0.57	10	21.135	23.715		
Distal Breadth	7.03	9.12	7.701	0.607	0.368	7.877	0.192	10	7.267	8.135		
Proximal Breadth	7.44	9.15	8.483	0.532	0.283	6.276	0.168	10	8.102	8.864		
Phalanx 3												
Greatest Length	21.14	30.16	24.391	3.018	9.107	12.372	1.067	8	21.868	26.915		
Distal Breadth	12.1	14.9	13.113	0.854	0.729	6.512	0.302	8	12.398	13.827		
Proximal Breadth	11.33	19.1	16.372	2.245	5.042	13.715	0.794	8	14.495	18.250		
Metapodium												
Width of Distal Condyle	8.52	10.53	9.474	0.594	0.352	6.266	0.171	12	9.097	9.851		
Width of Distal Trochlea	9.69	11.89	10.945	0.766	0.586	6.996	0.221	12	10.458	11.432		
Diameter of Distal Condyle	13.76	16.36	14.923	0.797	0.635	5.340	0.23	12	14.416	15.429		
Metatarsus												
Greatest Breadth of Proximal End			16.84					1				
Greatest Depth of Proximal End			17.86					1				
Scapula												
Greatest Breadth of Glenoid Process	25.15	29.62	26.927	1.596	2.549	5.929	0.652	6	25.251	28.602		
Greatest Breadth of Glenoid Cavity	16.90	21.59	19.034	1.564	2.446	8.217	0.591	7	17.588	20.481		
Astragalus												
Greatest Length of Lateral Half	25.08	27.96	26.617	1.450	2.102	5.447	0.837	3	23.015	30.218		
Greatest Depth of Lateral Half	15.26	16.42	16.013	0.653	0.427	4.078	0.377	3	14.391	17.636		
Graetest Breadth of Distal End	14.99	16.08	15.643	0.576	0.332	3.685	0.333	3	14.211	17.075		
Calcaneum												
Greatest Length			55.85					1				
Width of Articular Surface	17.05	17.24	17.145	0.134	0.018	0.784	0.095	2	15.938	18.352		
Elements	R		E	C		E	N	T				
Phalanx 1												
Greatest Length	36.35	45.66	41.300	2.221	0.493	5.378	0.398	31	40.486	42.116		
Distal Breadth	6.68	8.75	7.649	0.484	0.224	6.328	0.869	31	7.471	7.826		
Proximal Breadth	8.85	4.04	9.961	0.518	0.268	5.207	0.931	31	9.770	10.151		
Phalanx 2												
Greatest Length	19.15	24.52	21.565	1.359	0.184	6.302	0.262	27	21.027	22.103		
Distal Breadth	6.22	7.85	6.975	0.445	0.108	6.382	0.873	26	6.795	7.154		
Proximal Breadth	8.22	10.05	9.009	0.449	0.201	4.988	0.864	27	8.831	9.187		
Phalanx 3												
Greatest Length	23.91	29.43	26.126	1.448	0.209	5.545	3.161	21	25.467	26.862		
Distal Breadth	10.96	14.50	12.487	0.855	0.732	6.852	1.867	21	16.098	17.322		
Proximal Breadth	13.65	18.72	16.71	1.344	0.180	8.044	2.933	21	16.098	17.322		
Metacarpus												
Width of Distal Condyle	8.29	10.07	9.105	0.478	0.229	5.259	0.957	25	8.908	9.303		
Width of Distal Trochlea	9.88	12.23	10.851	0.621	0.386	5.728	5.243	25	10.594	11.108		
Diameter of Distal Condyle	14.04	16.57	14.948	0.683	0.467	4.572	1.367	25	14.666	15.231		
Metatarsus												
Greatest Breadth of Proximal End	17.96	21.14	19.443	0.945	0.894	4.865	1.972	23	19.034	19.852		
Greatest Depth of Proximal End	18.20	21.28	19.547	0.949	0.902	4.859	4.859	23	19.237	19.958		
Scapula												
Greatest Breadth of Glenoid Process	25.46	37.47	28.556	2.325	0.540	8.142	4.317	29	27.672	29.441		
Greatest Breadth of Glenoid Cavity	17.50	22.69	20.031	1.543	0.238	7.705	2.865	29	19.444	20.618		
Astragalus												
Greatest Length of Lateral Half	25.85	30.81	27.923	1.405	0.197	5.032	2.811	25	27.343	28.503		
Greatest Depth of Lateral Half	14.49	18.08	16.215	0.951	0.902	5.864	1.501	25	15.827	16.608		
Graetest Breadth of Distal End	14.30	16.81	15.478	0.662	0.438	4.278	3.242	25	15.204	15.751		
Calcaneum												
Greatest Length	54.14	65.38	58.223	2.940	0.864	5.050	6.001	24	56.981	59.464		
Width of Articular Surface	19.57	24.49	22.477	1.179	0.139	5.246	2.407	24	21.979	22.975		

Table 35

Measurements (in mm) of skeletal elements of *Gazella gazella* (Artiodactyla, Bovidae) compared with the recent form. n = number of specimens studied, x = mean, ∂ = Standard deviation, v = coefficient of variation, min = minimum value observed, max = maximum value observed, 95% lower = 95% confidence interval of the mean, 95% upper = 95% confidence interval of the mean.

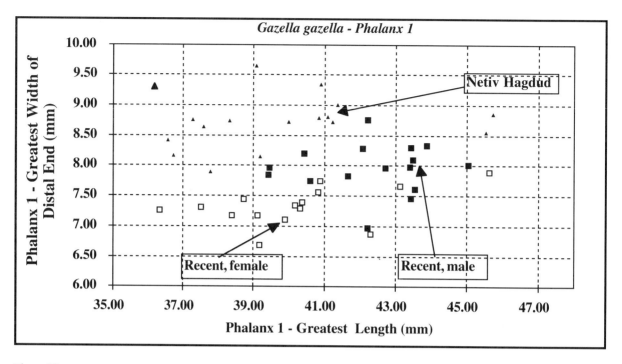

Figure 19
Plot of two variables of phalanx 1 in the mountain gazelle (*Gazella gazella*). It shows that the distal end of the first phalanx is significantly wider and mostly shorter in the PPNA population.

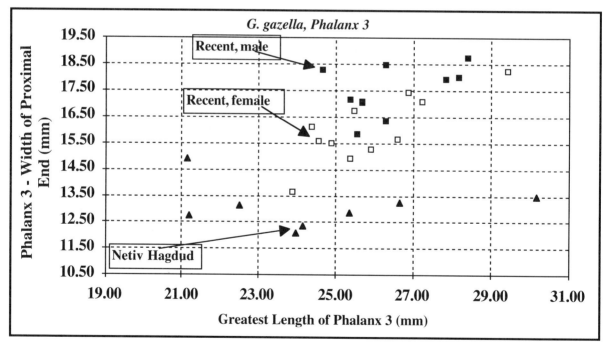

Figure 20
Plot of two variables of phalanx 3 in the mountain gazelle (*Gazella gazella*). It shows that the sexual dimorphism for the last phalanx is lower in the recent population, but there are differences in size and morphology of the phalanx between the two populations. In should be taken into account that in Netiv Hagdud most of the material (as known from horn cores) is from males.

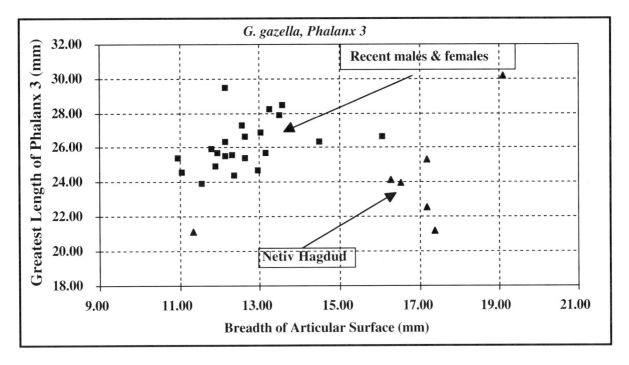

Figure 21
Plot of two variables of phalanx 3 in the mountain gazelle (*Gazella gazella*). It shows that the sexual dimorphism for the last phalanx is lower in the recent population, but there are differences in size and morphology of the phalanx between the two populations. In should be taken into account that in Netiv Hagdud most of the material (as known from horn cores) is from males.

may indicate some decrease in their cursorial capabilities. Extensive inbreeding (very few males were available for a lot of females) consequently brought about, among other morphological changes, shortening of the toes.

All of the horn core remains come from adult males. Seventeen skeletal elements from the 121 identified bones belonged to young animals, estimated to range between two to six months in age. Two bones (phalanx 2) were completely burned. Combining males and females, the total range of variability of phalanx 1 of the PPNA population is larger than that shown by recent ones (fig. 19). It is assumed that males, females, and young animals were hunted. Yet from the fact that all the horn cores found belonged to fully mature males it may be speculated that the majority of the hunted gazelles were males, and only a smaller fraction were females and young individuals. Thus, the Natufian tradition of selective male culling (Cope 1991) continued to be practiced by the local PPNA people, in spite of the radical decrease in hunting of large game and in particular of gazelle.

The distribution of *Gazella gazella* in the southern Levant changed completely during the Holocene. The question of past distribution of the eastern Mediterranean gazelles arose quite unexpectedly when Neolithic remains from the southern Sinai were found to belong to *Gazella gazella* rather than *Gazella dorcas*. *Gazella dorcas* presently occupies the Sinai peninsula and the central and southern region of the Negev and did so at least during the latter part of the Holocene (Dayan et al. 1986; Tchernov et al. 1986). *Gazella gazella* was also identified from other Neolithic sites located in the desert region such as Gilgal (PPNA) (Noy et al. 1980) and Jericho (PPNB) in the Lower Jordan Valley. It thus appears that there is no evidence for the existence of *Gazella dorcas* in the Pre-Pottery Neolithic or earlier periods in the southern Levant (Tchernov et al. 1986). The invasion of *Gazella dorcas* through the Nile Delta from North Africa was associated with a simultaneous wave of Saharan immigration of other elements that took place during the Holocene (Tchernov 1988). The swift increase in aridity during the post-Glacial period placed *Gazella dorcas*, once on the eastern bank of the Nile, in a physiological position superior to *Gazella gazella*. It did not take long before a new ecological balance was achieved and the two species parapatrically shared among them the mesic and arid belts of the southern Levant.

Alcelaphus buselaphus (Pallas, 1766)

Remains of hartebeest are not known from the nearby PPNA site of Gilgal (Noy et al. 1980), but there is other evidence to suggest that this large antelope survived along the Jordan Valley at least until the Middle Bronze Age. Clutton-Brock (1979) referred to a large antelope, but not an *Oryx*, from the PPNB of Jericho. A radius and a second phalanx of *Alcelaphus* were also described from two Middle Bronze Age phases at the site of Jericho (ibid.).

At Netiv Hagdud only one phalanx 2 was found in the Upper Area (tables 33, 34). This animal is always rare in any of the known Upper Pleistocene sites of the Levant. It is difficult to cope with the assumption that the paucity of remains in all prehistoric sites is due to its rarity in the wild, as this species is highly socialized and roams around the grazing fields in large herds. Rather it would be rational to argue that throughout the Upper Pleistocene, either people found this species difficult to hunt, or this species, for unknown reasons, was not popular.

Capra ibex Linnaeus, 1758

Remains of *Capra* are confined to one specimen (tables 33, 34) and are absent from the nearby site of Gilgal. Its size falls within the range of all the undomesticated *Capra* from Jericho (Clutton-Brock 1979). Like the rest of the non-gazelle material, this species was seldom hunted despite its probable common occurrence in the area. The present form, *Capra ibex nubiana*, mainly occupies the Dead Sea Rift Valley through Saudi-Arabia, Egypt, and the Sudan. Judging from other occurrences of *Capra ibex* in the Middle (Oumm Qatafa) and Upper Pleistocene assemblages in the Judean desert region (Vaufrey in Neuville 1951), this species has not been replaced since the Late Acheulian.

Suidae

Sus scrofa Linnaeus, 1758

At present no wild boar are known from this region, but the thickets of the marshy region and the tributaries flowing down the Dead Sea in the eastern and southern rims of the Dead Sea do contain populations of geographically isolated wild boar which are characterized by particularly small body size. These isolates were probably detached from the Mediterranean main stock during the Holocene. The existence of *Sus scrofa* in Netiv Hagdud and during the PPNA and the PPNB of Jericho (Clutton-Brock 1979) indicates that during these periods the Dead Sea populations of wild boar were still linked with the Mediterranean ones.

Sus scrofa is the second most common artiodactyl species in Netiv Hagdud (tables 33, 34) and seems to have been more popular among hunters than other artiodactyls, common enough to have been used as a relatively substantial food resource. Remains are too scarce, however, for a quantitative comparison with other populations.

In the nearby site of Gilgal the remains of wild boar are confined to one astragalum. Hecker (1975) described the remains of *Sus scrofa* from the PPNA of Beidha, a site located south and east of the Dead Sea.

Cervidae

Dama mesopotamica (Brooke, 1875)

Remains of the Mesopotamian fallow deer are confined to two finds (tables 33, 34): a tibia of a young animal and a fragment of maxillary. Remains of fallow deer were also found in Jericho from the PPNA to the Middle Bronze Age (Clutton-Brock 1979). *Capreolus capreolus*, which is absent both from Gilgal and Netiv Hagdud, is also mentioned from Jericho (ibid.), although only from the PPNA.

The existence of two species of deer in this region at the end of the Pleistocene and the dawn of the Holocene further supports the argument that the extension of the Mediterranean belt included the entire Dead Sea area.

Unidentified Artiodactyls

Unidentified remains of artiodactyls are confined to two bone fragments (tables 33, 34). The number of remains in general is too small to reach any conclusion regarding the relative frequency of skeletal elements in this group. But as far as *Gazella gazella* and, to a lesser extent, *Sus scrofa* are concerned, it seems that there is no preference for special exploitation of body parts in these species (table 34). Compared with the carnivores with the exception of cranial elements, the frequency of all other elements is more or less even. Cranial elements, metapodials, and phalanxes and, to a lesser extent, scapulae are the most common elements among the artiodactyls (fig. 18).

■

CHAPTER FOUR

CONCLUSIONS

■

The Density of Animal Remains in the Main Stratigraphic Complexes

The general representation of the main groups of animals across the major stratigraphic complexes is given in table 36 and in figures 22 and 23. Apart from the few remains of fishes which are absent from the Lower Complex, and the freshwater crabs which are difficult to quantify, all other groups of animals are represented throughout the sequence at the site. In the Upper Area (see site plan in fig. 2), most of the groups are poorly represented (table 36; figs. 22, 23) in comparison with the other complexes. This paucity cannot be explained as due to selective disintegration of the bone or shell material in the shallower part of the site. As presented in table 37, the number of elements per cubic meter (relative abundance per volume unit = density) of the smaller mammals (insectivores and rodents), as well as the density of the avian skeletal material (all of which possess delicate and fragile bones) in comparison with the remains of the large mammals (the artiodactyls), shows that much of the distribution is the same throughout the sequence of the Deep Sounding. There are no signs of differential deterioration of bone material throughout the sequence of the site. Within the Deep Sounding, the Middle Complex is the most productive stratigraphic unit for most of the groups (excluding fishes). Yet the relative abundance of each one of the main groups remains more or less the same as in other layers. As shown in figures 22 and 23, the differences in the relative density of most of the groups stays pretty much the same. As it is unreasonable to expect the artiodactyl bones to have a higher rate of disintegration, the higher concentration of smaller animals everywhere in the site indicates that differences in the abundance of animals are closely related to the original (anthropogenic and natural) accumulation factors and not to taphonomic processes. Following the taphonomic usages of Noe-Nygaard (1987) we assume that there is not much discrepancy between the life and the death assemblages. Bone exposure and weathering was minimal at this site.

The taxonomic composition, as well as the frequency of elements, does not show significant temporal

AREA	D E E P S O U N D I N G			UPPER AREA	Total
Species │ Complex	Lower Complex	Middle Complex	Upper Complex		
Mollusca					
Melanopsis praemorsa (costated)	40	114	11	325	490
Melanopsis praemorsa (smooth)	26	142	5	161	334
Unio terminalis	0	0	0	1	1
Amphibia					
Rana ridibunda	1	7	0	0	8
Reptilia					
Chameleo chameleon	1	7	0	0	8
Ophisaurus apodus	1	2	1	0	4
Agama stellio	0	2	2	0	4
Lacerta trilineata	0	1	1	0	2
Testudo graeca	0	1	0	0	1
Aves					
Fulica atra	0	1	0	0	1
Burhinus oedicnemus	0	1	0	0	1
Hoplopterus spinosus	0	9	0	0	9
Otis tarda	1	1	0	1	3
Columba livia	0	2	0	0	2
Streptopelia decaocto	1	6	1	0	8
Ciconia ciconia	1	16	1	0	18
Leptoptilus crumeniferos	0	1	0	0	1
Coturnix coturnix	7	98	10	5	120
Francolinus francolinus	1	13	1	1	16
Alectoris chukar	1	2	0	0	3
Ammoperdix heyi	3	1	0	0	4
Tadorna tadorna	44	150	8	13	215
Anas platyrhinchos	32	84	16	0	132
Anas querquedula	21	122	3	1	147
Anser albifrons	2	5	0	1	8
Milvus migrans	9	59	1	2	71
Pernis apivorus	2	4	0	0	6
Buteo rufinus	0	4	0	0	4
Buteo buteo	0	2	0	1	3
Aquila pomarina	1	2	1	0	4
Aquila spp.	1	3	1	1	6
Falco spp.	0	6	0	1	7
Circus sp.	0	1	1	0	2
Accipiter sp.	0	4	0	0	4
Galerida cristata	0	7	1	0	8
Melanocorypha calandra	0	3	0	0	3
Pycnonotus xanthopygos	0	1	0	0	1
Lanius excubitor	0	1	0	0	1
Turdus merula	0	2	0	0	2
cf. *Fringilla* sp.	0	1	0	0	1
Serinus serinus	2	0	0	0	2
Coccothraustes coccothraustes	0	2	0	0	2
Passer domesticus	0	1	0	0	1
Sturnus vulgaris	1	0	1	0	2
Onychognathus tristrami	0	0	1	0	2
Corvus cornix	68	209	2	6	285
Corvus monedula	13	14	0	0	27
Corvus ruficollis	0	2	0	0	2
Corvus rhipidurus	0	1	0	0	1
Pica pica	3	2	0	0	5
Mammalia					
Paraechinus aethiopicus	0	3	2	0	5
Hemiechinus auratus	1	11	4	0	16
Erinaceus concolor	2	7	2	0	11
Psammomys obesus	6	104	10	11	131
Meriones tristrami	0	31	14	0	45
Mus musculus	4	40	17	0	61
Spalax ehrenbergi	1	46	0	0	47
Arvicola terrestris	0	4	0	0	4
Microtus guntheri	0	1	0	0	1
Vulpes vulpes	11	89	28	24	152
Felis silvestris	0	8	3	3	14
Caracal caracal	0	2	0	0	2
Canis familiaris	0	2	1	0	3
Lepus capensis	11	5	12	26	84
Gazella gazella	6	78	1	36	121
Alcelaphus buselaphus	0	0	0	1	1
Sus scrofa	1	4	0	3	8
Dama mesopotamica	0	1	0	0	1
Capra ibex	1	0	1	0	2
Total	**327**	**1555**	**164**	**624**	**2670**

Table 36

The total number of identified specimens (NISP) of all the species and genera remains in the different complexes.

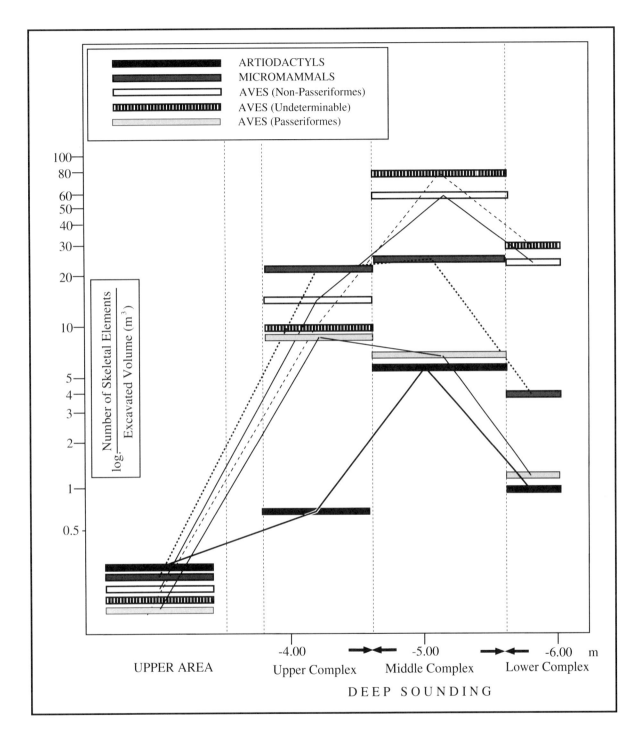

Figure 22
A general representation of the density of the artiodactyls, micromammals, and birds along the major stratigraphic units of the Deep Sounding and Upper Area of Netiv Hagdud.

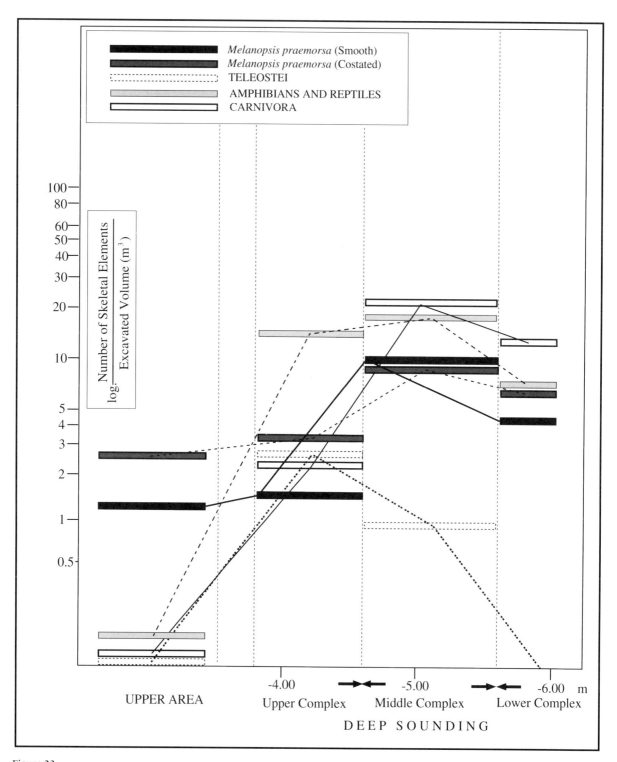

Figure 23
A general representation of the density of the fishes, amphibians, reptiles, fresh water molluscs, and carnivores along the major stratigraphic units of the Deep Sounding and Upper Area of Netiv Hagdud.

Area		Excavated Volume (m³)	E l e m e n t s p e r m³					
	Complex		Artiodactyla	Micromammals Insectivora Rodentia Lagomorpha	Carnivora	Aves Non-Passeriformes	Aves Passeriformes	Aves (Undetermined)
Upper Area		123.9	0.33	0.31	0.22	0.26	0.05	0.14
Deep Sounding	Upper Complex	3.0	0.66	21.66	10.66	15.33	2.33	10.66
	Middle Complex	12.7	6.53	22.76	7.95	54.88	21.02	21.02
	Lower Complex	6.5	1.23	4.00	1.69	21.85	14.5	31.85

Area		Excavated Volume (m³)	E l e m e n t s p e r m³			
	Complex		*Melanopsis praemorsa* (costated form)	*Melanopsis praemorsa* (smooth form)	Teleostei	Amphibians and Reptiles
Upper Area		123.9	2.82	1.24	0.01	0.05
Deep Sounding	Upper Complex	3.0	3.66	1.33	2.33	15.66
	Middle Complex	12.7	8.98	11.18	1.02	17.72
	Lower Complex	6.5	5.85	4.00	0.00	6.00

Table 37
Relative abundance of skeletal elements or shells (number of specimens/excavated volume) of the principal ecological groups in the main stratigraphical sequence of the site (see site plan in figure 2).

and spatial differences across the excavated areas. The relatively low density of animal remains in the Upper Area, despite its location much nearer to the surface, is not due to weathering, as the proportion of the remains of very small mammals to those of large mammals remains basically (spatially and temporally) the same throughout the sequence. The relatively low species diversity that is exemplified by the fossil assemblage of the Upper Area is due to their rarity in the deposits (probably caused by higher rate of deposition) rather than to differential weathering or changes in the community structure.

Those groups which are rare in the Deep Sounding are usually absent in the Upper Area. The pattern in which a few common species, with large numbers of individuals, are associated with many uncommon or rare species (represented in the record by a few, or only one, specimen), is a common structural pattern of any community. But when the availability of a sample is small or limited, a clear understanding of the ecological structure of the paleocommunity becomes difficult. However, the ratio between the number of species and some quantified "importance value" of the individual species which were retrieved from a fossil assemblage may be a useful device by which to better approximate the real species diversity. This is based mainly on the assumption that the basic ecological structure (the distribution pattern of species in the community) did not change much. In our case the time difference between the complexes was not long

enough to induce changes in the basic community structure. Indeed, the same common species are found throughout the sequence.

In order to compare the species diversity of Netiv Hagdud, we found that a good estimation can be reached by using the Wienner-Shannon index for general diversity: $H = -\sum (n_i/N.\log n_i/N)$, where n_i = "importance value" for each species (in our case the number of remains in the complex was evaluated); N = total of "importance value", (n_i/N may also be represented as the "importance value"—P_i—for each species, hence $H = -\sum(P_i \log P_i)$. In other words, this index is a mathematical statement of the evenness of the distribution of observations among a number of categories. If an assemblage has taxa represented but exhibits low diversity, as most of its fragments are restricted to one or a few taxonomic categories, and whereas a second assemblage has fragments more evenly spread over a smaller taxonomic range, it may exhibit high diversity. The relative diversity measure corrects for bias where there are different numbers of categories. A comparison of the diversity index of the different complexes is given in table 38. It shows that the indices are basically similar in all complexes. Species which are rare in the Middle Complex of the Deep sounding may be absent in other complexes or in the Upper Area. Yet if we assume that the ecological structure of the communities was basically the same, we would have needed about ten times more volume of deposit from the Upper Area in order to

AREA/COMPLEX	Total Number of Species	Total Number of Elements	Wienner-Shannon Index for General Diversity
UPPER AREA	20	624	0.3398
DEEP SOUNDING			
Upper Complex	31	164	0.1861
Middle Complex	63	1557	0.3136
Lower Complex	34	327	0.2577

Table 38
Comparison of the total number of species and total number of elements

obtain the same species diversity found in the much smaller volume of deposits of the Middle Complex.

In conclusion, the Upper Area is distinguished by low abundance and low density of animal remains. Apart from invertebrates, all mammals and birds are more or less similarly concentrated in the site. The highest relative density of remains is found in the Middle Complex of the Deep Sounding, where the most numerous groups are the non-passeriform birds. Astonishingly enough, most of the undetermined bird bones are concentrated in the Lower Complex probably due to their more fragmentary nature (table 37). The micromammals and the reptiles show almost the same density distribution in the Upper and Middle Complexes. The Deep Sounding shows for most of the groups a much higher density of remains, which in most cases amounts to one order of magnitude. But as the structures of the communities of the Upper Area and Deep Sounding are essentially similar, this salient change in the richness of remains cannot be considered a result of bone and shell disintegration. It is assumed that this similarity across the sequence, but with a disparity in density, is due to differences in human activities and rate of deposition in the different periods/areas of the site.

Distribution of Elements

If the weathering and the climatic factors seem to be insignificant in shaping the thanatocoenosis of this site which remained largely intact after burial, we may assume that the distribution of the skeletal elements of the vertebrates was originally determined by non-anthropogenic biotic factors as well as by mainly anthropogenic thanatic factors.

As for the gastropods, the relative density of shells of *Melanopsis praemorsa* remains largely the same through the sequence of the site. The tangible explanation is that both aquatic biotopes, a lake and river-

ine system, were more or less equally represented in the region. Ecotypes from both ecological systems (the costated lake form *M. praemorsa* and the smooth riverine form *M. praemorsa*) were constantly deposited in the village compound. There are no signs of using or altering these freshwater gastropod shells. It seems that they were either unintentionally collected by the people, or discarded/regurgitated by animals, or both.

Origins of the Biotic Deposits

The site of Netiv Hagdud cannot be considered altogether as a food refuse accumulation, but rather as mixed deposits from several sources. Exo- and endoskeletons (crabs, freshwater and land snails, and vertebrates) were deposited in situ as carcasses of natural populations or were transported naturally (by winds, floods, and rains) into the site area. All other components of the biotic deposits are either due to anthropogenic factors or to transport by predators. This picture is represented in a schematic way in figure 24.

The natural populations which could have been deposited in situ within the village limits, thus representing the biocoenotic component of the fossil assemblage, are from two completely different ecological media: aquatic and terrestrial.

The aquatic component includes a single crustacean species—*Potamon fluviatilis*. This species can forage out of any water body for some distance. It is attracted by food refuse but can easily fall prey to various predators or meet its death within the foraging range. The kitchen midden of the site could have been a trap for many crabs as is indeed indicated by the plethora of crab remains throughout the sequence of the site.

Freshwater molluscs in our case include mostly *Melanopsis praemorsa*, an obligatory aquatic species. Thus, the only possibilities for being buried in the site, other than the random or intentional collection and transportation by people, came 1) from having been washed down into the mound by natural agents like floods, 2) from dead shells being carried away by winds, or 3) from regurgitation by other animals. No signs of usage of these shells has been detected, so it seems that *Melanopsis* was of no known use to the local humans. Therefore we suggest that if not entirely deposited by natural transportation from nearby water sources, a reasonable explanation for the large

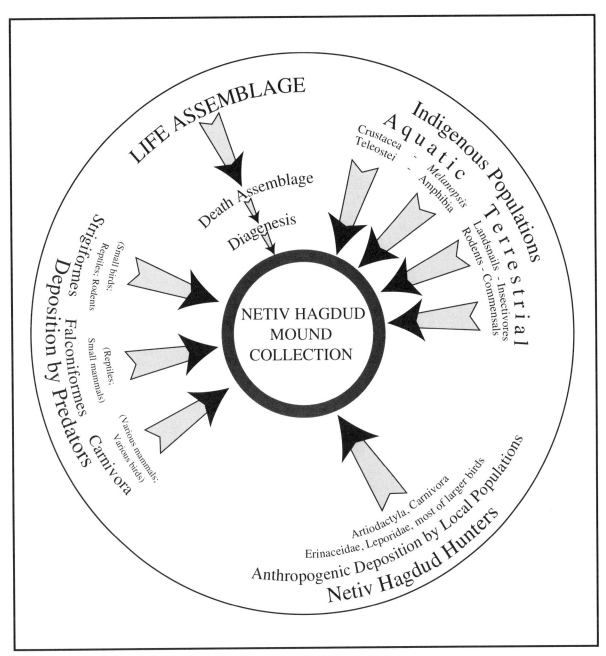

Figure 24
The various sources of biotic deposits in Netiv Hagdud.

numbers of shells in the site is that they were brought in when clay that already contained dead shells was quarried along the wadi channels in order to be used as building material (e.g., mud-bricks, adobe) and by rare transportation by animals.

Too few remains have been retrieved to claim fish as a food source. Although in the neighboring site of Gil-

gal (Noy et al. 1980) fish remains are also unknown, in layers 2 and 3 of Hatoula (early PPNA) Mediterranean species of large fishes (20–25 cm) were found and identified by Davis (1985). The few skeletal elements found in the site could have been transported either by predators (yet no fish eaters like kingfishers have been retrieved from this site) or by floods (fig.

24).

The only identified amphibian is *Rana ridibunda*, a species that is intimately connected to aquatic life. Rarely can these frogs forage on land. Therefore their existence in the site deposits could either have been due to natural transportation (floods) or to deposition by predators like the white stork (*Ciconia ciconia*), a species that is very common along the Dead Sea Rift Valley during the migratory period.

The species that constitute the main terrestrial in situ mortality and deposition are undoubtedly land snails. They may best represent the immediate indigenous fauna of this area, but have not yet been analyzed. We also have to consider that part of the terrestrial malacofauna can be accumulated in site deposits through winds and floods or gathered by some species of rodents. However, no gnawing marks have been found on the shells.

Commensal animals like *Mus musculus*, or some hedgehogs (Erinaceidae) are often attracted to food refuse and could have met their death within the site limits. The primitive dogs that were probably around the village could also be a part of the biocoenosis. Other animals like *Psammomys obesus*, an extremely specialized species with a very limited home range but with no ecological association with humans, may have lived within the site limits and contributed to the in situ deposition. A few species of other animals that are attracted to human refuse like foxes (*Vulpes vulpes*), grackles (*Onychognathus tristrami*), crows, and ravens, may constitute a dominant part of the biocoenosis. In this component we have also to include some birds of prey, in particular those species that are able to roost within the site like owls (*Athene noctua*) and falcons (*Falco* spp.). These species are not only part of the biocoenosis but are largely responsible for the transportation and deposition of many small birds, reptiles, and rodents to the site. As a rule these predators will sample the prey from a radius of about three kilometers. This is also accurate for carnivores like the red fox (*Vulpes vulpes*), a very common species in Netiv Hagdud and the most common carnivore in all Epipaleolithic and PPN sites. Closely associated with human settlements, at least some of their remains can be considered to be deposited in situ, while others could have been killed or hunted and transported by humans. The fox, as well as some of the cats, may also have been responsible for the accumulation of some species, particularly the commensal ones and those which were also attracted to food refuse within and around human settlements (*Mus musculus*, *Meriones tristrami*, and quite a few species of birds). However, evidence for natural modification of bones by carnivores (gnawing and digestion marks) is negligible. These carnivores did not stay in the area long enough to leave regurgitated or fecal material within the limits of the site. Therefore it seems that their contribution to the deposition of the commensal species, and other species that are associated with human settlements, is not great. Most of the carnivores found in the site were probably hunted and transported by the local people. There are too few specimens, however, to quantify the distribution of the skeletal elements of the carnivores in order to clarify this point.

The anthropogenic factor is the most significant in terms of biomass (fig. 24). The carcasses of most of the hunted animals, mainly birds and mammals, were selected and butchered outside the site area, probably in the hunting arena, and only the preferred portions were transported to the village (see next section). The methods of the local hunters must have been extremely versatile and highly sophisticated, as the array of animals that were caught and used is extensive, including very different taxa. Each would demand different hunting methods, high skill levels, detailed knowledge of game behavior, and the technological abilities to produce bows and arrows, nets, and other trapping and hunting devices. For hunting hares, ducks, crows and ravens, various artiodactyls, carnivores, and wild phasianids, completely different devices would have been needed. It is possible, of course, that there were specialized hunters for each one of these groups.

While the presence of the remains is attributed to humans, further cultural modifications tend to be relatively minor: the majority of the material is unburned and cut marks on bones are uncommon.

As mentioned above, and shown in a schematic way in figure 24, the post-depositional diagenetic processes were insignificant, and thus the proportion of the species and the skeletal elements may closely represent the distribution of the animal assemblage at burial. Due to leaching, however, conditions were completely different for the preservation of plants. Plants were only found in the Deep Sounding, generally 0.8 to 1.0 m below the surface (see Bar-Yosef and Gopher 1994).

ANIMAL EXPLOITATION—SPECIES AND ELEMENTS PREFERENCES

All major groups of animals, with the exception of aquatic animals, were exploited as food resources. The relative abundance of skeletal elements shows that for quite a few taxa, high selection for certain portions of the carcasses was practiced. Estimation of the abundance of the skeletal parts was based on the number of identified specimens (NISP) per species. The biomass of each species, however, was calculated on the basis of MNI.

Comparison of the main groups shows that the differences in the abundance of skeletal elements is not always explainable in terms of availability and amount of meat. Carnivores (fig. 18) show a higher frequency of cranial elements, and somewhat relatively more femora, tibiae, metapodials, and phalanxes, than other post-cranial bones. Carnivores could have been hunted for purposes other than as a food resource. As for the artiodactyls, there is an obvious preference for phalanxes and metapodials (fig. 18). The high frequency of cranial elements is mainly due to the collection of male gazelle horn cores, certainly not for dietary reasons. The fact that phalanxes are the most frequent element may indicate seasonal food shortages of the larger herbivores, particularly gazelles, the most common species in the ungulate assemblages. During the harsh summer period of the Dead Sea Valley, it would have been advantageous to look for more fat within the marrow of the proximal skeletal elements in order to avoid the deleterious effects of lean meat (Speth 1983, 1987, 1989). Thus, the high frequency of phalanxes may be explained as a nutritional preference rather than a technological one. Indeed, one possible reason for the extremely broad spectrum of animal species in the assemblage may be to ameliorate the consequences of having large herbivores with too lean meat, as is known from quite a few antelopes (Sinclair 1974, 1975), in the extremely seasonal climate of this region. In order to minimize their reliance on lean meat and thus avoid nutritional danger, hunter-gatherers had to find ways to augment their intake of fat by using distal skeletal elements and carbohydrates during times of stress and weight loss, possibly during the dry season (Speth 1983; Speth and Spielmann 1983).

As for local hares (*Lepus capensis*, figs. 17 or 18), metatarsals are significantly more abundant, while most of the other elements are more or less evenly represented. This may indicate a multi-purpose use of the carcasses (for both food and clothing).

When dealing with some common groups of birds, their purpose becomes much clearer. All groups of birds that show greater importance in terms of biomass (Anatidae, figs. 3, 4; Phasianidae, figs. 6, 7; and Corvidae, fig. 8; but not raptors, figs. 5, 6) also show a clear preference for the triosseum complex: scapula, coracoid, and sternum, on which the breast muscles, pectoralis major and pectoralis minor, are attached. Obviously, the purpose of carrying this special part of the body was for specific exploitation of the massive yet very lean meat of the breast. Some other less common non-passeriform groups of birds show as well a much higher frequency of the pectoral girdle.

For the raptors a different selective attitude is exemplified by the relative frequency of their skeletal elements (figs. 5, 6, 25). In most of the species of this group, legs (tarsometatarsi but in particular the phalanxes) were more frequently selected and transported to the home base, while coracoids and sterni of most of the raptors are largely absent. It is only in *Milvus migrans* (and the unidentified raptors, the majority of which may nonetheless belong to *Milvus migrans*) that the pectoral elements are very common (fig. 25). Therefore it is assumed that kites were also used as a food source similar to ducks by tearing the pectoral muscles out of the carcass. Obviously the local inhabitants handled most of the raptors differently. The body part frequencies of these birds indicate that quite often, and in contrast with the ducks, they did transport the whole body (except the skull) to the site area (fig. 25). For most of the other species of raptors there was a preference for legs, mainly phalanxes, from which the sharp claws could have been used as tools (Solecki and McGovern 1980).

Although the spectrum of food resources is extremely broad, in terms of biomass the artiodactyls, including gazelles (and as a second priority the wild boar) exceed all other groups of animals (fig. 26). However, if taken as a whole, the bird biomass falls very close to that of the artiodactyls. Yet it is worth noting that in comparison with Natufian sites where the importance of gazelles in terms of biomass is extremely high and may amount to 95 percent, in many PPNA sites the importance of gazelles and other large mammals significantly decreases. This information is not yet fully quantified and is based mainly on the data given by Legge (1972), Bouchud (1987), and

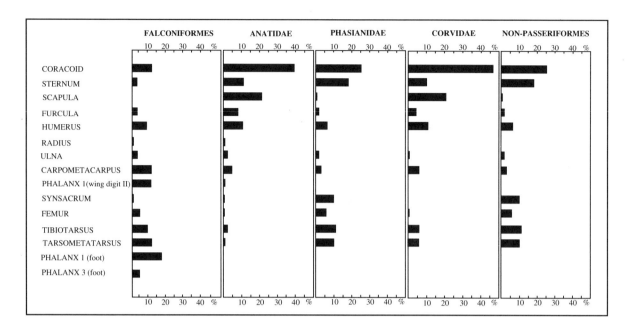

Figure 25
Relative representation of skeletal parts of different groups of birds. There is a sharp difference in the exploitation of the body parts for different groups of birds.

Henry (1989a). The assemblage of Netiv Hagdud, however, clearly shows that there is a decrease in the importance of gazelles as a food resource during this period.

NATUFIAN AND PPNA FAUNAL ASSEMBLAGES—A COMPARISON

While large mammals are apparently fully represented in each of the PPNA sites where at least some faunal analysis has been carried out, representation of micromammals, as well as most other vertebrate groups, is heavily biased. In most of the sites larger mammals will be almost fully retrieved due both to the better chance of preservation of their bones and to their greater size. Thus, even in the older excavations, archaeologists were able to collect large bone assemblages in which the representation of the species diversity was complete. Yet, for the recovery of a sample where most of the microvertebrates will be faithfully represented, careful sieving is required. From tables 39 and 40 it is obvious that the absence of most of the micromammals and birds from Gilgal and Jericho, which are geographically close at hand, is due to the recovery methods of the excavation rather than

their absence in the region. Table 39 shows that there is not much similarity in the PPNA megafaunas between the site of Jericho and Netiv Hagdud, which are separated by a mere 13 km as the crow flies. *Bos primigenius* is absent only from Netiv Hagdud, and in spite of its rarity it is found in all other PPNA sites. *Equus* sp. (probably *E. hemionus*) and *Capreolus capreolus* were reported from the PPNA of Jericho (Clutton-Brock 1979) but are absent from all the other PPNA sites (table 39). *Procavia capensis* was only recorded from the site of Gilgal (Noy et al. 1980).

In general this disparity in the faunal lists is due to the great unevenness of the assemblages rather than to biological, geographical, or cultural factors. Thus, dealing with the PPNA faunal assemblages from the Lower Jordan Valley as a whole may furnish us with a more comprehensive picture of the animal communities of this region during the turn of the Pleistocene. This picture is utterly different from the present communities of this region. In most of the PPNA sites of the southern Levant, the smaller mammals, as well as the passeriform birds (tables 39 and 40), either have not yet been thoroughly studied (Hatoula), represent samples that are too small to permit meaningful study (Gilgal, Salibiya IX), or were retrieved using old archeological methods which resulted in insufficient microfaunal material (Jericho). All this restrains us

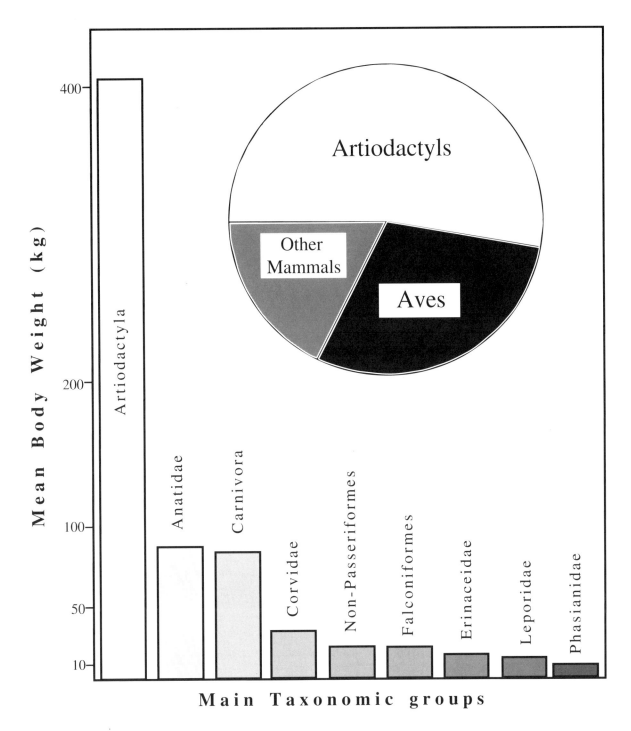

Figure 26
The spectrum of food resources in terms of biomass. Although artiodactyls (and among them the gazelle) exceed all other groups of animals, taken as a whole, the biomass of birds falls very shortly behind them, indicating their great importance as food resource.

NETIV HAGDUD	GILGAL (Noy et al. 1980)	JERICHO (Clutton-Brock 1979)	SALIBIYA IX (Horwitz, pers. comm)	HATOULA (Davis 1985)
L o w e r J o r d a n V a l l e y				M e d i t e r r a n e a n
Insectivora	**Insectivora**	**Insectivora**	**Insectivora**	**Insectivora**
-	-	Erinaceidae, Undet.	-	-
Erinaceus concolor	*Erinaceus concolor*	-	*Erinaceus concolor*	*Erinaceus concolor*
Hemiechinus auritus	*Hemiechinus auritus*	-	*Hemiechinus auritus*	-
Paraechinus aethiopicus	-	-	-	-
Rodentia	**Rodentia**	**Rodentia**	**Rodentia**	**Rodentia**
			Rodentia spp. (undet.)	-
-	-	*Jaculus jaculus*	-	-
Psammomys obesus	-	-	-	-
Meriones tristrami	-	-	-	-
Spalax ehrenbergi	-	-	*Spalax ehrenbergi*	*Spalax ehrenbergi*
Mus musculus	-	-	-	-
Arvicola terrestris	*Arvicola terrestris*	-	-	-
Microtus guentheri	-	-	-	*Microtus guentheri*
Lagomorpha	**Lagomorpha**	**Lagomorpha**	**Lagomorpha**	**Lagomorpha**
Lepus capensis	*Lepus capensis*	*Lepus capensis*	*Lepus capensis*	*Lepus capensis*
Hyracoidea	**Hyracoidea**	**Hyracoidea**	**Hyracoidea**	**Hyracoidea**
-	*Procavia capensis*	-	-	-
Carnivora	**Carnivora**	**Carnivora**	**Carnivora**	**Carnivora**
			Carnivora sp. (undet.)	
-	-	-	-	*Vormela peregusna*
-	-	-	-	*Meles meles*
-	-	*Martes foina***	-	-
Vulpes vulpes	*Vulpes vulpes*	*Vulpes vulpes*	*Vulpes vulpes*	*Vulpes vulpes*
Canis familiaris	-	*Canis familiaris*	-	-
-	*Canis aureus*	-	-	-
Felis silvestris	-	*Felis silvestris*	-	*Felis* cf. *silvestris*
Caracal caracal	-	*Caracal caracal*	-	-
-	-	*Felis chaus*	-	-
Artiodactyla	**Artiodactyla**	**Artiodactyla**	**Artiodactyla**	**Artiodactyla**
Sus scrofa	*Sus scrofa*	*Sus scrofa*	*Sus scrofa*	*Sus scrofa*
-	*Bos primigenius*	*Bos primigenius*	-	*Bos primigenius*
Capra ibex	-	*Capra* sp.	-	-
Gazella gazella	*Gazella gazella*	*Gazella gazella* *	*Gazella gazella*	*Gazella gazella*
Alcelaphus buselaphus	-	-	-	?*Alcelaphus buselaphus*
-	-	-	-	? *Ovis*
Dama mesopotamica	*Dama mesopotamica*	*Dama mesopotamica*	-	-
-	-	*Capreolus capreolus*	-	-
Perissodactyla	**Perissodactyla**	**Perissodactyla**	**Perissodactyla**	**Perissodactyla**
-	-	*Equus* sp.(?*hemionus*)	-	-

Table 39
Comparative mammalofaunal list of several PPNA sites in the Lower Jordan Valley (Jericho, Gilgal, and Netiv Hagdud), and from the Mediterranean region in the Latroun (Judea) area.

*Reanalysis of the gazelles from Jericho showed that they belong to *Gazella gazella* (Tchernov et al.1986) rather than *G.dorcas* (Clutton-Brock 1979).
**M. tmartes* in Clutton-Brock 1979. Reanalysis of the Jericho carnivores has shown that they actually belong to the southern Levantine species, *M. foina*.

from overall detailed microfaunal comparisons for the PPNA period. Altogether it seems that the assemblages of large- and medium-size mammals and of the non-passeriformes are basically the same in terms of ecological occupation and preferences by the early Neolithic hunters.

A comparison of the relative frequencies of the ungulate species in PPNA and a few Natufian sites is

NETIV HAGDUD	GILGAL (Noy et al. 1980)	JERICHO (J. Blandermar & G.S.Cowles, personal communication)	HATOULA (Pichon 1989)
L o w e r J o r d a n V a l l e y			Mediterranean
Non-Passeriformes	**Non-Passeriformes**	**Non-Passeriformes**	**Non-Passeriformes**
-	-	-	*Podiceps cristatus*
-	-	-	*Pelecanus onocrotalus*
-	-	-	*Crex crex*
-	-	-	*Porzana* sp.
Fulica atra	-	-	-
Hoplpopterus spinosus	*Hoplpopterus spinosus*	-	
-	-	-	*Tringa nebularia + sp.*
-	-	-	*Gallinago* sp.
-	-	-	*Scolopax rusticola*
-	-	*Numenius arquata*	-
-	-	*Anthropoides virgo*	-
-	-	*Chlamydotis undulata*	-
Otis tarda	-	-	-
Leptoptilus crumeniformes	-	-	-
-	-	-	*Ardea cinerea*
-	-	-	*Egretta alba*
-	-	*Ciconia niger*	-
Ciconia ciconia	-	-	*Ciconia ciconia*
-	-	*Columba oenas*	-
Columba livia	*Columba livia*	-	-
Streptopelia decaocto	*Streptopelia* sp.	-	-
Tadorna tadorna	*Tadorna tadorna*	-	-
-	-	*Anas crecca*	*Anas crecca*
Anas querquedula	*Anas* sp.	-	*Anas querquedula*
Anas platyrhynchos	*Anas platyrhynchos*	*Anas platyrhynchos*	*Anas platyrhynchos*
Anser albifrons	*Anser albifrons*	-	*Anser* sp.
-	-	*Cygnus cygnus*	-
-	Falconiformes Undet.	-	-
-	-	*Milvus milvus*	-
Milvus migrans	-	*Milvus migrans*	*Milvus migrans*
Pernis apivorus	-	-	-
Buteo buteo + rufinus	*Buteo* cf. *buteo*	-	*Buteo buteo + rufinus*
Aquila pomarina	-	-	-
Aquila spp.	-	*Aquila clanga + chrysaetus + sp.*	-
Falco spp.	-	-	-
Circus sp.	-	-	-
Accipiter sp.	-	*Accipiter nisus + gentilis*	*Accipiter nisus + gentilis*
-	-	-	?*Perdix* sp.
Alectoris chukar	*Alectoris chukar*	*Alectoris chukar* + sp.	*Alectoris chukar*
Francolinus francolinus	-	-	-
Ammoperdix heyi	-	-	-
Coturnix coturnix	-	*Coturnix coturnix*	*Coturnix coturnix*
-	-	-	*Asio otus*
-	-	-	*Tyto alba*
-	-	-	*Strix aluco*
Ahtene noctua	-	-	-
Passeriformes	**Passeriformes**	**Passeriformes**	**Passeriformes**
Galerida cristista	-	-	-
Melanocorypha calandra	-	-	-
Pycnonotus xanthopygos	-	-	-
Lanius excubitor	-	-	-
Turdus merula	-	-	-
Serinus serinus	-	-	-
Coccothraustes coccothraustes	-	-	-
cf. *Fringilla* sp.	-	-	-
Passer domesticus	-	-	-
Sturnus vulgaris	-	-	-
Onychognathus tristrami	-	-	-
Corvus corone	*Corvus corone*	-	*Corvus corone*
Corvus rufficollis	-	-	-
Corvus rhipidurus	-	-	-
Corvus monedula	-	*Corvus monedula*	-
-	-	*Corvus frugilegus*	-
Pica pica	-	-	-

Table 40
Comparative avifaunal list of several PPNA sites in the Lower Jordan Valley (Jericho, Gilgal, and Netiv Hagdud), and from the Mediterranean region in the Latroun (Judea) area.

Alectoris barbara never existed in the Southern Levant, and was never sympatric with it. The only species that existed in this region throughout the Middle and Upper Pleistocene of the Levant is *Alectoris chukar*.

presented in table 41. Although all the Natufian material was calculated on the basis of MNI while the PPNA material was calculated on NISP counts, it seems that during the Natufian the preference for gazelles, in comparison with other ungulates although not in terms of absolute meat weight, increased in time from a minimum of 57 percent in the earlier Natufian of Hayonim Cave to 90 percent in Netiv Hagdud. Consequently the percentage of all other ungulate species, particularly the cervids, decreased. Preferences for wild boar (*Sus scrofa*) remained largely the same (table 41). The frequencies of wild goats and ibexes range only from 2.5 percent to 6.1 percent, and the steppe and savanna dwellers, like *Equus* sp. and *Alcelaphus buselaphus*, are always low.

Jericho

The detailed results of the excavations of Jericho (fig. 1) demonstrate the presence of oval and rounded semi-subterranean dwellings built of cobbles, plano-convex mudbricks, wooden beams, and some sort of plaster similar to that at Netiv Hagdud. (For general sources on the site of Jericho, see Kenyon 1957; Kenyon 1981; Kenyon and Holland 1983; Bar-Yosef 1986; Bar-Yosef et al. 1991.)

The list of species for the PPNA of Jericho is given in tables 39, 40, and 41. As in other PPNA sites, at Jericho *Gazella gazella* was the predominant species killed for food (Clutton-Brock 1971, 1978, 1979). Clutton-Brock (1979) argued that these gazelles were not controlled by humans as suggested by Legge (1972) but that their exploitation may have been

accomplished by means of drives and surrounds as described by Henry (1975).

Additionally, *Vulpes vulpes* was very common in the PPNA assemblage, and according to Clutton-Brock (1979) was used for food (table 42). Similar to Netiv Hagdud, large game mammals (*Alcelaphus buselaphus*, *Dama mesopotamica*, *Capreolus caperolus*, *Bos primigenius*), large felids, *Capra ibex*, and *Equus* sp. (*hemionus*) were not common in the record (table 41). Sheep/goat proportions during this period are low (4.3 percent), yet the existence of sheep, in particular wild sheep, in these strata should be reevaluated. The only goat known from this region throughout the late Middle and Upper Pleistocene is *Capra ibex*.

Gilgal

Situated on an elongated ridge, the site of Gilgal is located near Netiv Hagdud (fig. 1), surrounded by the same habitats and exposed to much the same environmental conditions. Remains of oval, semi-subterranean dwellings and other structures were uncovered from the site (Noy et al. 1980; Bar-Yosef et al. 1991). Relatively large quantities of wild barley and oats were retrieved from what could have been a silo (Bar-Yosef and Kislev 1989; Bar-Yosef et al. 1991; see also Part I of this series).

The faunal assemblage of Gilgal is essentially similar to that of Netiv Hagdud (tables 39, 40, 41) (Noy et al. 1980). The majority of species that occupied the area of Gilgal no longer exist in the Lower Jordan Valley; most of them have retreated northward, some no longer inhabiting the southern Levant region. Most of the aquatic, woodland, and grassland dwellers disappeared from the region; only the rock dwellers, which

UNGULATE SPECIES	NAHAL OREN PPNA (Legge 1972; Noy et al.1973) (NISP=516)	JERICHO PPNA (Clutton-Brock 1979) (NISP=397)	GILGAL PPNA (Noy et al. 1980) (NISP=11)	NETIV HAGDUD PPNA (NISP= 133)	HATOULA KHIAMIAN (Cope, in press) (MNI=21)	NATUFIAN (MNI=67)	HAYONIM CAVE TERRACE (early) NATUFIAN (late) (Cope, in press) (MNI=101) (MNI=166)		EYNAN (=MALLAHA) NATUFIAN (Cope, in press) MNI=65
Gazella gazella	87.9	74.50	72.72	90.08	71.0	70.0	57.0	64.7	58.2
Capra aegagrus*/ibex**	3.1	2.50**	-	1.5**	4.0*	2.9*	5.5*	2.5*	6.1*
Bos primigenius	1.6	8.55	9.09	-	9.5	5.9	4.5	6.0	4.6
Cervus elaphus	0.2	-	-	-	-	4.4	-	0.6	4.6
Dama mesopotamica	2.9	0.25	9.09	0.75	4.0	5.9	5.5	15.3	6.1
Capreolus capreolus	0.8	0.50	-	-	-	5.9	19.5	5.4	6.1
Sus scrofa	3.5	13.60	6.02	6.02	9.5	-	4.5	5.4	13.8
Alcelaphus (cf) buselaphus	-	0.25	0.75	0.75	-	1.5	2.5	-	0.25
Equus spp.	-	0.25	-	-	4.0	-	1.0	0.6	0.25

Table 41

Relative frequency of ungulate species (given in percentage) in several PPNA (including Khiamian) and Natufian assemblages in Israel.

* = *Capra aegagros*, ** = *Capra ibex*, NISP = Number of bones, MNI = Minimum number of individuals.

PPNA Sites	Salibiya IX [a]		Jericho [b]		Netiv Hagdud [c]		Hatoula [d] (Layers 2-3)	
SPECIES	NISP	%	NISP	%	NISP	%	NISP	%
Vulpes vulpes	6	7.0	128	89.5	152	28.7	5	11.9
Canis spp. *(lupus + familiaris)*	-	-	8	5.6	3	0.5	-	-
All Other Carnivores	16	18.6	7	4.9	16	3.0	2	4.8
Lepus capensis	50	58.1	-	-	84	15.8	7	16.7
Rodentia	5	5.8	-	-	244	46.0	15	35.6
Insectivora	9	10.5	-	-	32	6.0	13	31.0
Lepus / All Ungulates	0.657	65.7	-	-	0.641	64.1	0.026	2.6
Vulpes / All Ungulates	0.079	7.9	0.356	35.6	1.160	116.0	0.018	1.8

Table 42
The number of identifiable specimens and the relative frequency of carnivores and small mammals in several southern Levantine PPNA sites.

a. Horwitz and Tchernov, unpublished data.
b. Clutton-Brock 1971, 1978, 1979.
c. Tchernov, unpublished data.
d. Davis 1985.

are *a priori* better adapted to arid conditions, have survived there (*Procavia capensis*). Similar to Jericho and Netiv Hagdud, waterfowl provided an important source of food (tables 39, 40). The remains of large game mammals such as aurochs, deer, and boar, although not present in great numbers, indicate almost indiscriminate hunting of wild animals, except for relatively large numbers of gazelles. As with Netiv Hagdud, there is evidence for intentional culling of mature male gazelles. Waterfowl, hares, and gazelles were the predominant source of protein for Gilgal's inhabitants, but a large variety of small reptiles, birds, and mammals also contributed to their diet, indicating a reliance on a very broad spectrum of animals.

Salibiya IX and Gesher

Next to Gilgal and Netiv Hagdud, the site of Salibiya IX was discovered and produced an assemblage defined by the excavators as a "Khiamian" lithic assemblage. A small human figurine from the site resembled those from Nahal Oren, Gilgal, El-Khiam Terrace, and Mureybet (Bar-Yosef 1980a). The paucity of the faunal remains did not permit a detailed analysis and comparison with PPNA or other sites.

Located in the Central Jordan Valley, the site of Gesher (fig. 1) is a small village consisting of rounded huts that was occupied only for a single, short phase (Garfinkel 1990; Horwitz and Garfinkel 1992). The archaeological layer contained lithic artifacts (Khiamian points, Hagdud truncations, sickle blades, a small number of backed and Helwan lunates, and bifacially shaped axes or adzes), grinding and pounding tools, and evidence of dwelling structures.

The faunal collection is too small for detailed intersite spatial comparisons, yet shows general similarities with the other PPNA sites in the Jordan Valley. *Gazella gazella* is the predominant large mammal. *Bos primigenius* and *Sus scrofa* are also present. Of the smaller mammals *Lepus capensis*, *Vulpes vulpes*, and *Spalax ehrenbergi* were noted (Horwitz and Garfinkel 1992). A few unidentifiable avian and reptilian bones were also recorded, and much like all other PPNA sites along the Jordan Valley, claws of the freshwater crab *Potamon fluviatilis* are very common.

Hatoula

The Khiamian of Hatoula (layers 2-3), as argued by the excavators (Ronen and Lechevallier 1985, 1991; Lechevallier et al. 1989; Lechevallier and Ronen 1985, 1989), seems to be characterized by a shift within the

Late Natufian toolkit through the introduction of El-Khiam points and the more intensive use of awls, while the low frequencies of sickle blades remained unchanged.

Six species of ungulate were present in layers 2-3 (tables 39, 40, 41). *Gazella gazella* remains constitute 71 percent of the megafaunal collection, indicating the continuing economic importance of that species. *Bos* is the most important in terms of meat weight. As in layers 4-5 of the Late Natufian, an unusually high percentage of gazelles were immature. According to Cope (1991), 65.5 percent of gazelles were under one year of age at the time of death. The bias for the male gazelle has completely disappeared by the Khiamian, resulting in size means and most V-values being once again normal. A comparison of the relative frequency of skeletal parts of gazelles and goats in several PPNA sites is represented in table 43, showing a high preference for phalanxes and metapodials. Although there are differences between Hatoula and Netiv Hagdud in the relative representation of gazelle skeletal elements, they are not very significant and are most probably due to the different methods employed for analysis, counting, and calculations of the skeletal elements by different authors. It is worth noting that when compared to later PPNB sites in Sinai, (table 43; see details in Tchernov and Bar-Yosef 1982 and Dayan et al. 1986), there are no essential differences in the representation of skeletal elements of *Gazella gazella* and *Capra ibex* between those PPNB sites and the PPNA of Hatoula and Netiv Hagdud.

The faunal analysis of the site of Hatoula done by Davis (1985) has shown some differences between the PPNA and the Natufian assemblages: a relatively higher proportion of birds and fish (and possibly hare, too) and increased quantities of larger fish in the PPNA (for the relative frequencies of hares and foxes see table 42). Davis (1985) also stresses that there was an increase in hunting of smaller animals and fish by more sophisticated techniques. Otherwise, the Natufian and Khiamian large mammal assemblages show a striking similarity, suggesting that no significant changes in the basic concepts of exploitation of large mammals, and no significant climatic changes took place.

A comparison of the percentage representation of skeletal elements of birds between a few Natufian sites and Netiv Hagdud shows some differences in the treatment of birds during the two periods. In the case of ducks, it seems (table 44) that there was much less preference for special elements and body parts during the Natufian. Foot elements were more common during the Natufian, while forelimbs and elements connected with the pectoral muscles, although already very much preferred, were not as often selected as in

SITES	Hatoula (Layers 2-3) (a)		Hatoula (Layers 2-3) (b)		Netiv Hagdud (c)		Wadi Tbeik (d)						Ujrat el Mehed (e)					
	P		P N		A		P				P		N		B			
Species	*Gazella gazella*		*Gazella gazella*		*Gazella gazella*		*Capra ibex*		*Gazella gazella*		*Capra + Gazella*		*Capra ibex*		*Gazella gazella*		*Capra + Gazella*	
Skeletal Elements	n	%	n	%	n	%	n	%	n	%	n	%	n	%	n	%	n	%
Skull and Mandible	30	7.2	-	-	4	4.3	8	3.9	-	-	15	4.2	43	2.3	12	11.2	349	14.3
Scapula	12	2.7	13	5.2	8	8.6	-	-	-	-	4	1.1	48	2.6	2	1.9	104	4.2
Humerus	50	12.0	21	8.5	5	5.4	10	4.8	3	3.6	17	4.7	104	5.7	1	0.9	121	4.9
Ulna + Radius	32	7.8	7	2.8	1	1.1	-	-	1	1.2	6	1.7	173	9.5	-	-	203	8.3
Calcaneum + Astragalum	30	7.3	22	8.9	5	5.4	21	11.5	3	3.6	19	5.3	154	8.4	-	-	168	6.8
Carpalia	10	2.4	15	6.0	3	3.2	-	-	-	-	6	1.7	33	1.8	-	-	72	2.9
Phalanxes	106	26.7	119	48.0	39	41.9	124	60.7	63	75.9	219	61.1	409	22.5	5	4.7	414	16.8
1	40	9.7	76	30.7	20	21.5	59	28.8	13	15.6	73	20.4	235	12.9	1	0.9	236	9.6
2	37	9.0	-	-	10	10.7	40	19.6	37	44.7	108	30.1	30	1.6	3	2.8	33	1.3
3	29	7.0	43	17.3	9	9.7	25	12.3	13	15.6	38	10.6	144	79.0	1	0.9	145	5.9
Pelvis	2	0.5	17	6.9	2	2.2	-	-	-	-	-	-	77	4.2	-	-	109	4.6
Femur	27	6.5	-	-	1	1.1	4	1.9	-	-	5	1.4	80	4.4	-	-	101	4.2
Tibia	24	5.7	12	4.8	4	4.3	6	2.9	5	6.0	18	5.0	-	-	78	72.9	96	3.9
Tarsalia	25	6.1	-	-	-	-	-	-	-	-	-	-	-	-	-	-	-	-
Metapodia	63	15.1	22	8.9	21	22.5	31	14.3	8	9.7	49	13.8	702	38.6	9	8.4	715	29.2
Total	411	100	248	100	93	100	204	100	83	100	358	100	1823	100	107	100	2462	100

Table 43
Skeletal elements representation by number of specimens and percentage in *Gazella gazella* and *Capra ibex* from several PPNA and PPNB sites in the southern Levant.

a. Cope 1991 and personal communication.
b. Davis 1985.
c. Tchernov, unpublished data.
d. Tchernov and Bar-Yosef 1982.
e. Dayan et al. 1986.

the PPNA of Netiv Hagdud. For both the raptors (table 45) and the Phasianidae (table 46), no definite preference is shown among the Natufian sites, and it seems that there is not a common "Natufian tradition." High selectivity of elements could have been initiated only during the PPNA, but unfortunately detailed analyses of bird bones are only available for Netiv Hagdud.

In summary, there are clear differences between the Natufian and the PPNA. The lithic industry of the PPNA has much lower frequencies of microliths everywhere, even in desertic sites such as Abu Madi I in southern Sinai (Bar-Yosef 1985). Other differences are manifest in the shapes of sickle blades, the presence of bifacial tools in village sites, well-polished stone celts, and changes in types and frequencies of grinding and pounding tools. The economic base for the PPNA was a mixture of cultivation of emmer, barley, and legumes. Fruits and wild seeds were collected including nuts and acorns. Plant remains indicate the practice of cultivation of wild barley and the systematic gathering of seeds and fruits in the region up to

10 km around each site. Specialized hunting and trapping of large varieties of animals, but in particular water birds, as well as selective hunting of gazelles, and some fishing in a few sites, provided the meat component in the diet (Bar-Yosef et al. 1991). Gazelle was still the primary game animal in the Mediterranean belt, while in the arid zone both ibexes and gazelles constituted the main protein source. Other big game, such as *Dama mesopotamica*, *Bos primigenius*, *Sus scrofa*, and in a few sites equids and *Alcelaphus buselaphus*, comprised a relatively small portion of the protein sources, much as in the Natufian period. Mainly waterfowl and hares, but also a wide array of smaller vertebrates, continued to comprise a significant portion of the diet.

A large collection of animal bones was recovered from Ganj Dareh in central Iran. The fauna was analyzed by Hesse (1984) who reported a process of goat domestication in the tenth millennium B.P. What interests us is that even during a period of early herding of goats, the basic composition of the fauna from this site, especially from layers E to A (eleventh to late

Anatidae	Netiv Hagdud[a] PPNA		Mallaha (=Eynan) [b] Natufian		Mureybet [b] Natufian	
Skeletal Elements	**n**	**%**	**n**	**%**	**n**	**%**
Coracoid	219	38.7	53	19.2	78	15.9
Scapula	129	22.8	24	8.7	42	8.5
Sternum	64	11.3	-	-	10	2.0
Furcula	39	6.9	8	2.9	-	-
Humerus	67	11.8	43	15.6	73	14.9
Radius	4	0.7	4	1.5	14	2.8
Ulna	-	-	41	14.9	98	19.9
Carpometacarpus	20	3.5	28	10.2	123	24.9
Wing phalanx 2	1	0.2	14	5.1	15	3.0
Synsacrum	1	0.2	-	-	-	-
Femur	4	0.7	3	1.1	5	1.0
Tibiotarsus	6	1.1	43	15.6	27	5.5
Tarsometatarsus	1	0.2	13	4.8	8	1.6
Cranial elements	10	1.7	2	0.7	-	-
Total	**566**	**100**	**276**	**100**	**493**	**100**

Table 44

Number of skeletal elements and their percentage representation in the family Anatidae in Natufian and PPNA sites.

a. Tchernov, unpublished data. Based on the following species: *Anas platyrhynchos, Anas querquedula, Anser albifrons.*

b. After Pichon 1984, 1987. Based on the following species: *Anas platyrhynchos, Anas querquedula, Anas clypeata, Anas crecca, Marmonetta angustirostris, Aythya spp., T. tadorna, Bucephala.*

SITES	Netiv Hagdud [a] P P N A		Hayonim [b] Natufian		Mureybet [b] Natufian	
Skeletal Elements of Falconiformes	n	%	n	%	n	%
Coracoid	19	12.7	2	2.5	-	-
Scapula	-	-	3	3.7	1	1.4
Sternum	6	4.0	-	-	-	-
Furcula	3	2.0	14	17.3	-	-
Humerus	13	8.7	-	-	4	5.6
Radius	1	0.7	-	-	2	2.8
Ulna	7	4.7	1	1.2	-	-
Carpometacarpus	17	11.3	5	6.2	5	6.9
Wing phalanx 2	16	10.7	1	1.2	3	4.2
Synsacrum	1	0.7	-	-	-	-
Femur	7	4.7	6	7.4	-	-
Tibiotarsus	13	8.7	9	11.1	2	2.8
Tarsometatarsus	18	12.0	20	24.7	8	11.1
Foot phalanxes	29	19.1	20	24.7	47	65.2
Cranial elements	-	-	-	-	-	-
Total	**150**	**100**	**81**	**100**	**72**	**100**

Table 45

Number of skeletal elements and their percentage representation in the Falconiformes in Natufian and PPNA sites.

> a. Tchernov, unpublished data. Based on the following species: *Milvus migrans, Buteo* spp. + *Pernis apivorus, Aquila* spp., *Falco* spp. +*Accipiter* spp., and undetermined Falconiformes.
> b. Pichon 1984, 1987. Based on the following species: *Buteo* spp., *Aquila* spp., *Falco* spp.

Skeletal Elements	*Coturnix coturnix*		*Francolinus + Alectoris + Ammoperdix*		*Alectoris chukar*		*Coturnix coturnix*		*Alectoris chukar*	
SITES	Netiv Hagdud [a] P P N A				Hayonim Cave [b] Natufian				Mureybet [b] Natufian	
Skeletal Elements	n	%	n	%	n	%	n	%	n	%
Cranial elements	-	-	-	-	11	2.2	-	-	1	3.6
Coracoid	35	28.9	12	55.2	51	10.3	9	25.0	10	35.6
Sternum	34	28.1	1	4.6	15	3.0	2	5.6	-	-
Scapula	1	0.8	-	-	22	4.4	2	5.6	3	10.7
Furcula	2	1.7	1	4.6	13	2.6	-	-	-	-
Humerus	11	9.1	1	4.6	34	6.9	5	13.8	1	3.6
Ulna	1	0.8	1	4.6	12	2.4	1	2.8	2	7.2
Radius	-	-	-	-	3	0.6	-	-	-	-
Carpometacarpus	1	1.7	1	4.6	36	7.3	3	8.4	1	3.6
Wing phalanx 2	-	-	-	-	8	1.6	-	-	-	-
Pelvical elements	-	-	-	-	5	1.0	-	-	-	-
Femur	5	4.1	-	-	9	1.8	-	-	-	-
Tibiotarsus	18	14.9	1	4.6	214	43.3	5	13.9	8	28.5
Tarsometatarsus	12	9.9	4	17.2	62	12.6	9	25.0	2	7.2
Total	**121**	**100**	**22**	**100**	**495**	**100**	**36**	**100**	**28**	**100**

Table 46

Number of skeletal elements and their percentage representation in the Phasianidae in Natufian and PPNA sites.

> a. Tchernov, unpublished data.
> b. Pichon 1984, 1987.

tenth millennium B.P., Hesse 1984), is astonishingly similar to the PPNA assemblages of the Lower Jordan Valley. Table 47 represents the faunal list from Ganj Dareh as adapted from Hesse's (1984) report. In spite of being familiar with domestication, the people of Ganj Dareh continued the sophisticated and specialized hunting practices seemingly very similar to those of the PPNA people of the Jordan Valley. Thus, the Natufian tradition of specialized hunting did not cease abruptly during the early stages of domestication (see also Edwards 1989; Tchernov 1984, 1991a). It is also worth noting that the commensal house mouse (*Mus musculus domesticus*) was found both in Netiv Hagdud and Ganj Dareh, indicating long-lasting occupations of these sites (Hesse 1975; Auffray et al. 1988, 1990).

The economy of early Neolithic farming communities was based, as most authorities agree, on the cultivation of cereals and legumes, the collection of wild seeds and fruits, and extensive hunting and trapping of a wide range of animals. The hunted animal species were essentially the same across the southern Levant, always dominated by gazelles. It was only during the following millennium (PPNB) that animal exploitation shifted toward high proportions of *Capra* and *Ovis*, due to a significant decrease in the number of gazelles. The cultivation of emmer, wheat, and barley is attested to at Tell Aswad, but barley is also found at Jericho, Netiv Hagdud, and Gilgal. While in these sites the charred seeds are often identified as domesticated, Mureybet produced mainly wild species. Legumes were also cultivated but their state of domestication is still not clear. Extensive and intensive gathering of wild seeds and wild fruits, as well as of wide varieties of small and large wild vertebrates continued in this period.

It is far more difficult to appreciate the proportional amount of vegetarian food consumed by the local populations in this area. Legumes could have been a most important component (Kislev and Bar-Yosef 1988), but evidence supporting this contention is very rare in the PPNA of the Lower Jordan Valley. In the PPNA of Jericho only two lentils were identified by Hopf (Zohary and Hopf 1988).

From a cultural aspect, the remnants of cultivated barley (*Hordeum distichon*) along with brittle barley (*Hordeum spontaneum*) which were uncovered from Netiv Hagdud (Kislev et al. 1986; Kislev and Bar-Yosef 1988) are more important, proving that the early cultivation of these cereals already emerged during the

GANJ DAREH (Central Iran)	
Layers E–A (9th to late 8th millenium B.C.)	
(Adapted from Hesse 1984)	
AVES	**MAMMALIA**
Non-Passeriformes	*Erinaceus concolor*
Phalacrocorax carbo	*Hemiechinus auritus*
Rallus aquaticus	*Myotis blythi*
Charadriiformes (undet. spp.)	*Lepus capensis*
Anas platyrhynchos	*Ellobius fuscocapillus*
Anas crecca	*Meriones* sp.
Anas querquedula	*Mus musculus*
Anas sp.	*Canis aureus*
Aquila sp. (large)	*Vulpes vulpes*
Aquila sp. (small)	*Ursus arctos*
Falco cf. *tinnunculus*	*Meles meles*
Accipitidae (undet).	*Felis chaus*
Grus sp.	*Sus scrofa*
Otis tarda	*Cervus elaphus*
Alectoris chukar	*Gazella* sp.
Tetraogallus caspius	*Bos primigenius*
Columba cf. *palumbus*	*Ovis orientalis*
Pterocles orientalis	*Capra aegagrus*
cf. *Tyto alba*	**REPTILIA**
Passeriformes	*Testudo* sp.
Corvus corone	*Varanus griseus*
Passriformes (undet. spp.)	*Ophisaurus apodus*
AMPHIBIA	Lacertidae (undet)
Ranidae (undet.)	**TELEOSTEI**
INVERTEBRATA	undet. small sp.
Unionidae (undet.)	
Freshwater Crustacea (undet.)	

Table 47
The composition of species in the Neolithic of Ganj Dareh. There is much similarity with the faunal assemblages of the PPNA sites in the Lower Jordan Valley.

early tenth or late eleventh millennium B.P. in the Lower Jordan Valley. The existence of early plant domestication at Netiv Hagdud is based on the large amount of kernels and rachis segments, in particular those segments showing irregular (artificial) fractures (Kislev et al. 1986).

SEASONALITY

Seasonal activities determined on the basis of bird, mammal, and seed remains can provide general information about the duration of the hunting and gathering seasons. Along the boundaries of the Mediterranean-Saharo-Arabian belts, seasonal differences are more distinct due to the sharp climatic changes that limit the reproductive cycles and other biological activities of local biota that are reflected in the site.

The list of birds (table 48) supports the general conclusion that hunting must have taken place throughout the year in order to get this variety of species. Table 48 provides the obligatory occurrence of the species in the area. The seasonal activities of the avifauna given in this list and in figure 27 are based on distributions known mainly until 1950, when the massive destructive human intervention occurred in the Lower Jordan Valley.

Among the mammals, *Gazella gazella* provides important seasonal information. Reproduction of *Gazella gazella* seldom occurs throughout the year. As a rule there is a seasonal peak during the rainy period (Baharav 1974, 1981, 1983a,b). Females may experience a postpartum estrus and give birth twice a year only if some ecological conditions (such as the availability of water throughout the year) materialize (ibid.). Females reach sexual maturity during the first year of life (Baharav 1983a,b), and often bear their first fawn at 18 months of age. Males, however, are seldom reproductive before the ages of three or four years old. In all gazelle populations, territoriality of dominant breeding males is characteristic and pronounced (ibid.). Territoriality and related reproductive activities are most pronounced from November to January. During this time the adult male population increases. From January to May when all females are pregnant, the population of adult males decreases sharply. Spring and early summer are thus the main period when most fawns are born. The age of the few remains of fawns recovered from the assemblage of Netiv Hagdud that could be ascribed was one to three months. Therefore, they most probably were hunted between March and July (fig. 27).

Among the plant remains, sufficiently concentrated amounts of rachis fragments (including glumes and spikelets) of cultivated *Hordeum distichon*, along with brittle barley (*Hordeum spontaneum*) (Kislev et al. 1986), enable us to estimate the reaping season of cereals, while still unripe, during the PPNA of Netiv Hagdud (fig. 27). The ecological distribution of the wild ancestor of barley, traditionally grouped in *Hordeum vulgare spontaneum* (*sensu* Zohary and Hopf 1988), is particularly common in the dry summer deciduous oak park-forest belt and on the slopes facing the Jordan Rift Valley and thus would have been very common around Netiv Hagdud during the PPNA period. Additionally, pips of *Ficus carica* identified from the site (Kislev et al. 1986) indicate gathering activities of figs during late summer (fig. 27) (see also Zohary and Hopf 1988).

The collective evidence indicates all-year, long-term activities at the area, a situation that enabled the existence of synanthropic and commensal animals within and around the site.

COMMUNITY STRUCTURE, PALEOECOLOGY, AND PALEOENVIRONMENTAL IMPLICATIONS

The faunal assemblages of Netiv Hagdud, as well as those recorded from the other PPNA sites within the Lower Jordan Valley (Gilgal, Salibiya, and the PPNA layers of Jericho), reveal the existence of an ecosystem completely different from the present one. The only way to understand the remarkable composition of the faunal assemblages of these sites is to assume that entirely different climate and environmental conditions prevailed during this period. In order to support an essentially Mediterranean spectrum of animals in an area that at present is basically arid and occupied by typical Eremian species, a swift and profound climatic change from a mesic to an arid regime must be assumed. Indeed, the fossil record of Netiv Hagdud, and all other PPNA sites in the area, leaves no doubt as to the environmental conditions that sustained these biota.

The rich ecosystem of the Lower Jordan Valley during the Last Glacial, although well adapted to the relatively predictable environment in which it evolved during the colder phases of the Upper Pleistocene, was not able to resist the more punctuated abiotic disturbances at the dawn of the Holocene. It is now widely accepted that the glacial periods were highly variable in the temperate zone and lower latitudes (Garner 1975; Walker and Chen 1987; Rull 1990) but were of a remarkable magnitude along the Mediterranean-Eremian tropical suture lines (Tchernov 1982, 1988). The southern Palearctic desert belt shifted northward and southward over large regions alternately enriching and impoverishing those marginal areas. Thus, the Lower Jordan Valley was one of the regions that constantly underwent dynamic biogeographic fluctuations due to global and local climatic changes.

Species	J	F	M	A	M	J	J	A	S	O	N	D
Fulica atra	mmm	mmm	mm						mmm	mmm	mmm	mmm
Hoplopterus spinosus			+	+++	+++	+++	+++	+++	+++			
Otis tarda		*	*							*	*	*
Ciconia ciconia	mmm	mmm	* * *						* * *	mmm	mmm	mmm
Tadorna tadorna	mmm	mmm	* * *	*					*	* * *	mmm	mmm
Anas querquedula			*	* * *	* * *		*	* * *	* * *	*		
Anas platyrhynchos	mmm	mmm	* *						* * *	*	mmm	mmm
Milvus migrans	mmm	mmm	* * *	* * *	+++	+++	+++	+++	* *	+++	+++	+++
Pernis apivorus					* * *	* * *			*	* * *		
Buteo buteo	mmm	mmm	* * *	*					* * *	mmm	mmm	mmm
Buteo rufinus	+++	+++	+++	+++	+++	+++	+++	+++	+++	+++	+++	+++
Aquila pomarina			* * *	* * *					* * *	* *		
Athene noctua	+++	+++	+++	+++	+++	+++	+++	+++	+++	+++	+++	+++
Columba livia	+++	+++	+++	+++	+++	+++	+++	+++	+++	+++	+++	+++
Streptopelia decaocto	+++	+++	+++	+++	+++	+++	+++	+++	+++	+++	+++	+++
Coturnix coturnix	mmm	mmm	mm	+++	+++	+++	+++	+++	* * *	* * *	mmm	mmm
Ammoperdix heyi	+++	+++	+++	+++	+++	+++	+++	+++	+++	+++	+++	+++
Alectoris chukar	+++	+++	+++	+++	+++	+++	+++	+++	+++	+++	+++	+++
Francolinus francolinus	+++	+++	+++	+++	+++	+++	+++	+++	+++	+++	+++	+++
Turdus merula	mmm	mmm	mmm	......	......	......	......	......	mmm	mmm	mmm	mmm
Galerida cristata	+++	+++	+++	+++	+++	+++	+++	+++	+++	+++	+++	+++
Melanocorypha calandra	+++	+++	+++	+++	+++	+++	+++	+++	+++	+++	+++	+++
Pycnonotus xanthopygos	+++	+++	+++	+++	+++	+++	+++	+++	+++	+++	+++	+++
Lanius excubitor	+++	+++	+++	+++	+++	+++	+++	+++	+++	+++	+++	+++
Serinus serinus	mmm	mmm	mmm						mmm	mmm	mmm	mmm
Passer domesticus	+++	+++	+++	+++	+++	+++	+++	+++	+++	+++	+++	+++
Coccothraustes coccothraustes	mmm	mmm	mm						mmm	mmm	mmm	mmm
Onychognathus tristrami	+++	+++	+++	+++	+++	+++	+++	+++	+++	+++	+++	+++
Sturnus vulgaris	* * *	* * *	* *						* * *	* * *	* * *	* * *
Pica pica *	+++	+++	+++	+++	+++	+++	+++	+++	+++	+++	+++	+++
Corvus monedula	mmm	mmm	mm						mmm	mmm	mmm	mmm
Corvus ruficollis	+++	+++	+++	+++	+++	+++	+++	+++	+++	+++	+++	+++
Corvus rhipidurus	+++	+++	+++	+++	+++	+++	+++	+++	+++	+++	+++	+++
Corvus corone **	+++	+++	+++	+++	+++	+++	+++	+++	+++	+++	+++	+++

Table 48
The present (early 20th century) occurrence of bird species year-round in the region of the Lower Jordan Valley.
 mmm = migratory species—peak of migration, mm = migratory species—low rate of migration, ... = probable occurrence, *** = wintering species, +++ summer breeding and resident species).
> (* Non-migratory birds, extinct at present but should have been residents during the PPNA period [see text]).
> (** Non-migratory species which retreated to the Mediterranean belt, and should have been residents during the PPNA period [see text]).

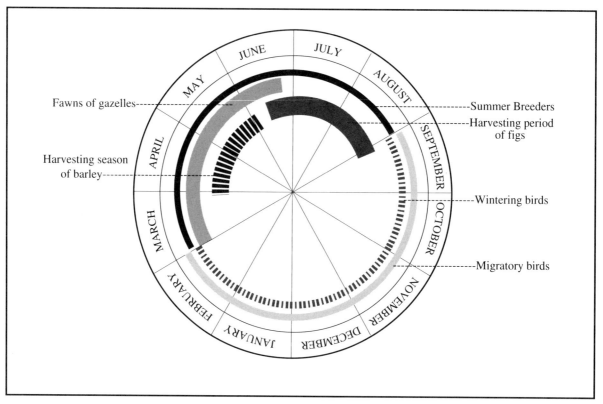

Figure 27
Seasonal activities of birds, mammals, and plant foods provide general information about the duration of the hunting and gathering activities of the Netiv Hagdud community.

The herpetofaunal list recorded from Netiv Hagdud is given in table 49. None of the recorded species presently lives in the area. This fauna represents a typical Mediterranean pattern of distribution with preference for moist habitats. Distribution is generally limited by the minimum 300 mm isohyet. *Lacerta trilineata* and the eastern subspecies *Chameleo chameleon rectristrictus* are wood dwellers, while the large-size legless lizard *Ophisaurus apodus* and the common tortoise *Testudo graeca* are limited mainly to batha and garigue (chaparal) landscapes. The present distribution of *Lacerta trilineata*, as shown in figure 28 clearly indicates a significant west-north withdrawal of this distinctive Mediterranean species.

The presence of *Rana ridibunda*, an obligatory aquatic frog (table 49); a large quantity of the freshwater crustacean *Potamon fluviatilis*, the opisthobranch mollusc *Melanopsis praemorsa*; the fanule of fishes; and the rich assemblage of aquatic birds clearly indicates that bodies of freshwater were in abundance during this period in the vicinity of the PPNA sites in the Lower Jordan Valley.

Tables 50, 51, and 52 summarize the present distribution of all the non-passeriform and passeriform taxa that have been recorded from Netiv Hagdud. Worth noting is the impressive mixture of species originating in remote biogeographical realms. Palearctic, Oriental, Ethiopian, as well as some endemic Levantine species of birds coexisted in this region. Status among these species is diverse, including miscellaneous migratory birds, wintering birds, summer breeders, and residents. Many of them are definitely extralimital taxa (table 52), and apart from migratory species that constantly use the old Syro-African migratory route on their way to Africa and back to Eurasia, the avifaunal turnover during the Holocene is remarkable.

Many species of birds share their daily activities between several, sometimes extremely different, habitats, mainly for breeding, roosting, and feeding. Starlings, for instance, nest solitarily in holes but feed commonly in meadows by probing their bills deep into the topsoil. On winter grounds they roost on trees and feed in large flocks. Thus, in different eco-

Species	Geographic Range	Regional Distribution	Isohyet	Habitat
Amphibia				
Rana ridibunda	Central Palearctic, circum-Mediterranean	Mediterranean, semiarid and freshwater bodies around the Dead Sea		Aquatic
Reptilia				
Chameleo chameleon	Near and Middle East, North Africa and Spain	*C.c.rectristricta* - Mediterranean *C.c.musae* - western Negev	*C.c.r.* - 350 *C.c.m.* -150	Arboreal
Ophisaurus apodus	Eastern Palearctic and Levant	Mediterranean	300	Batha and garigue
Agama stellio	Near and Middle East and Arabian peninsula	Mediterranean to semiarid disjunctive distribution		Rock dweller
Lacerta trilineata	Near and Middle East	Mediterranean	350 - 400	Wood
Testudo graeca	Circum Mediterranean and Levant	Mediterranean	350	Batha

Table 49
Present regional distribution, habitat preference, minimum-maximum isohyet, and local distribution status of the reptiles and anurans recorded from Netiv Hagdud.

topes the avian community will function differently. Exploitation of the habitat changes from species to species. In order to reconstruct the old landscape and interpret the past habitats, two main functional habitats have been taken into consideration separately: feeding grounds and breeding grounds. The partitioning of the habitats in the two different grounds is given in table 53. A dominant component of the avian community shows high preference for arboreal, aquatic, grassland, and moist habitats. The present avian community of the Netiv Hagdud area is predominantly Eremian. The limiting habitat feature for breeding, roosting, and feeding of some of the species (*Corvus corone*; *Pica pica*; *Sturnus vulgaris*, which are obligatory colonial during the winter roosting periods; *Coccothraustes coccothraustes*; *Serinus serinus*; and *Turdus merula*) is the existence of large trees.

The aquatic and semi-aquatic components of the avifaunal assemblage indicate not only the existence of bodies of freshwater in the vicinity but also the great ecological variety these water bodies must have had in order to maintain species like *Fulica atra*, *Hoplopterus spinosus*, different species of ducks (*Anas* spp.), geese (*Anser albifrons*), marabou, and storks.

Table 48 shows the status of the birds species in the region of Netiv Hagdud during the PPNA and at present. The list clearly indicates that many of the species no longer exist anywhere in the region, so that the avian community must have changed profoundly sometime after the PPNA. Among the resident and non-migratory species, 29 percent are no longer found in the area. One, *Pica pica*, became extinct in the

whole Levantine province. About 40 percent are at present only rarely recorded from the region. The rest of the species still exist in the Lower Jordan Valley as residents. Among the 11 species of the summer birds, 10 are not known at present from the area, one of which, *Leptoptilus crumeniformes*, is extinct in Asia. Among the 20 wintering and migratory species, 14 species (70 percent) are absent from the entire region. The communities that still exist in this region consist mainly of Eremian birds, or those migratory species that constantly use the Syro-African Rift Valleys as their main migratory route.

Similarly, the micromammal community underwent a profound change in the pattern of their distribution. Out of the 9 recorded species, 7 (table 54) no longer exist in the region and are found only within the Mediterranean belt, one of which became extinct in the southern Levant (*Arvicola terrestris*). *Paraechinus aethiopicus* is rare in the Lower Jordan Valley, while the other two species of hedgehogs (*Hemiechinus auritus* and *Erinaceus concolor* withdrew from the region during the Holocene (fig. 29). Except for *Psammomys obesus*, all recorded rodent species are restricted at present to the Mediterranean belt, as is well exemplified by the present distribution of *Microtus guentheri* (fig. 30).

Table 55 displays the list of the medium to large mammals which were recorded from all the PPNA sites within the Lower Jordan Valley. Of the 19 species, nine are absent from the region, or became extinct in the southern Levant (*Capreolus capreolus*, *Equus hemionus*, and *Dama mesopotamica*), and *Alcela-*

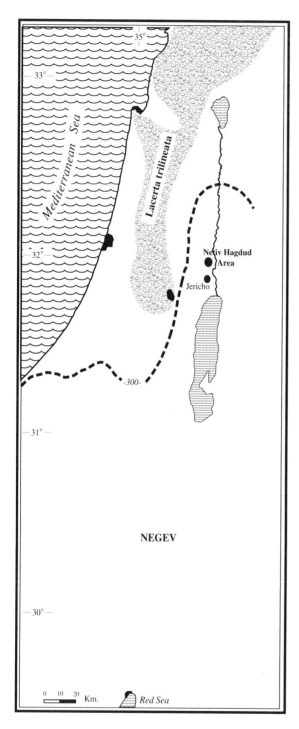

Figure 28
The present distribution of *Lacerta trilineata*, a typical
Mediterranean species, which is recorded at Netiv Hagdud,
and the suggested borderline for the 300 mm isohyet during
the PPNA.

phus buselaphus in Asia. Six of the 19 species are
unknown or are very rare at present in the region of
the Lower Jordan Valley, and only four species are
regularly recorded at present from the valley. The
enormous retreat of *Martes foina* (recorded from Jericho) as opposed to the status quo in the distribution
of *Capra ibex nubiana* is given in figure 31.

Figure 32 portrays the average annual precipitation
of Israel. The Lower Jordan Valley in general stays at
present around the 100 (± 25) mm isohyet, while the
300 mm line demarcates the ecological borderland
between the essentially semiarid ecosystems and the
Mediterranean ones. This map can be compared with
the pattern of distribution of all the recorded species
from the PPNA sites in the Lower Jordan Valley in
order to evaluate and appreciate the extent of change
since the early Neolithic in the ecological regime for
each one of the species. Most of these no longer exist
in this region and are limited by the minimum isohyet, often at the 300 mm line or above. If the ecological amplitude of the Mediterranean elements that
was recorded from the Lower Jordan Valley is restricted to ± 300 mm rainfall, the logical implication is
that the Lower Jordan Valley during the PPNA period
(the sites of Gilgal, Salibiya IX, Netiv Hagdud, and
Jericho) was well within the Mediterranean regime
(fig. 33).

The conspicuous shift of the Mediterranean region
during the PPNA into the Eremian belt of the Levant
is supported by other evidence. Palynological analyses
of Salibiya IX (Leroi-Gourhan and Darmon 1987; Darmon 1988; Darmon et al. 1989) have shown a marked
development of trees around 8,000 B.P., suggesting relatively forested conditions during the Netiv Hagdud
period until 11,840 B.P. In Salibiya IX, Leroi-Gourhan
and Darmon (1987) identified the following trees:
Quercus calliprinos, *Fontanesia* (Oleaceae), *Ceratonia*, as
well as representatives of the aquatic Nympheaceae.
Ficus carica was also identified from Salibiya IX (Bar-
Yosef et al. 1991; Kislev et al. 1986; Kislev and Bar-
Yosef 1988). In Netiv Hagdud the arboreal pollen
amounts to 21 percent (Leroi-Gourhan and Darmon
1987; Darmon 1988; Darmon et al. 1989), all of which
belongs to the Mediterranean flora with the dominance of Oleaceae, while aquatic plants
(Nympheaceae) distinctively increased. Darmon
(1988) argued that in general the pollen analyses
from the area indicate that the somewhat drier Late
Natufian was followed by a wet period, marked by a
significant increase of trees and water plants and a

Species	Biogeographic Distribution	Regional Distribution	Present Status in the Southern Levant
Non-Passeriformes			
Fulica atra	Palearctic, Oriental & Australian	Inland waters of the Levant	Wintering and rare resident
Hoplopterus spinosus	Ethiopian & Levantine	Wetlands of the southern Levant	Essentially resident
Otis tarda	Palearctic	Northern Levantine steppes	Essentially absent
Leptoptilus crumeniformes	Ethiopian		Absent
Ciconia ciconia	Palearctic	Mediterranean belt and Jordan-Dead Sea valleys	Wintering & Migratory
Columba livia	Holarctic	Trans-Levantine	Resident
Streptopelia decaocto	Oriental-Levantine	Trans-Levantine	Resident
Tadorna tadorna	Palearctic	Trans-Levantine	Wintering
Anas querquedula	Palearctic	Trans-Levantine	Migratory
Anas platyrhinchos	Holarctic	Trans-Levantine	Wintering, rare resident
Anser albifrons	Holarctic	Trans-Levantine	Wintering, migratory
Milvus migrans	Palearctic, Paleotropic, Australian	Trans-Levantine	Wintering, migratory, and a rare summer breeder
Pernis apivorus	European	Trans-Levantine	Migratory
Buteo buteo	North-Palearctic	Trans-Levantine	Migratory
Buteo rufinus	South-Palearctic	Trans-Levantine	Essentially resident
Aquila pomarina	Oriental-Eastern Palearctic	Trans-Levantine	Migratory
Alectoris chukar	South-eastern Palearctic	Trans-Levantine	Resident
Francolinus francolinus	Oriental	Jordan-Dead Sea Valleys	Resident
Ammoperdix hey	Southern Levantine	Jordan-Dead Sea valleys	Resident
Coturnix coturnix	Trans-Palearctic	Mediterranean	Migratory and resident
Athene noctua	Trans-Palearctic	Trans-Levantine	Resident

Table 50
Present distribution and status of non-passeriform birds from Netiv Hagdud.

Species	Biogeographic Distribution	Regional Distribution	Present Status in the Southern Levant	Isohyet (mm)
Passeriformes				
Galerida cristata	Southern (temperate) Palaearctic + Northern Ethiopia	Mediterranean to Semiarid	Resident	
Melanocorypha calandra	Temperate Palearctic	Mediterranean to Semiarid	Resident + wintering Populations	Min. 170
Pycnonotus xanthopygos	Trans-Levantine	Mediterranean + Oases	Resident	
Turdus merula	Trans-Palearctic + Oriental	Essentially Mediterranean	Resident + (wintering)	Min. 250*
Lanius excubitor	Holarctic + Oriental	Jordan-Arava Valleys + Negev	Resident	
Serinus serinus	European + West North Africa	Mediterranean	Wintering + (recent summer Breeders)	Min. 400
Coccothraustes coccothraustes	Trans-Palearctic	Mediterranean	Wintering	Min. 400
Passer domesticus	Sub-Cosmopolitan	Commensal	Resident	
Sturnus vulgaris	Palearctic	Mostly Mediterranean	Wintering	Min. 250
Onychognathus tristrami	Southern Levantine	Dead Sea + Red Sea Rifts	Resident	Max. 70
Pica pica	Holarctic + Southern Arabia	Absent	Absent***	
Corvus monedula	Palearctic	Mediterranean	Wintering (+resident **)	Min. 400
Corvus ruficollis	Saharo-Arabo-Sindian	Southern Levantine Deserts	Resident	Max. 250
Corvus rhipidurus	Ethiopian + Southern Levantine	Dead Sea Rift Valley	Resident	Max. 70
Corvus cornix	Palearctic	Mediterranean	Resident	Min. 400

Table 51
Present distribution and status of passeriform birds from Netiv Hagdud.
* In non-anthropogenic sites.
** A few isolated populations.
*** Extinct in the southern Levant, except one endemic population in southern Arabia.

Residents, Non-Migratory Birds	PPNA	Present	Summer Birds	PPNA	Present	Wintering and Migratory Birds	PPNA	Present
Columba livia	+	+	Fulica atra	(?)	-	Fulica atra	+	-
Streptopelia decaocto	+	+	Hoplopterus spinosus	+	-	Hoplopterus spinosus	+	-
Alectoris chukar	+	(+-)	Otis tarda	(+?)	-	Otis tarda	+	-
Francolinus francolinus	+	(+-)	Leptoptilus crumeniformes	(+?)	(†)	Leptoptilus crumeniformes	+	(†)
Ammoperdix heyi	+	(+-)	Coconia ciconia	(+?)	-	Ciconia ciconia	+	+
Athene noctua	+	+	Anas platyrhinchos	(+?)	-	Tadorna tadorna	+	-
Galerida cristata	+	(+-)	Milvus migrans	+	-	Anas querquedula	+	-
Melanocorypha calandra	+	-	Buteo rufinus	+	(+?)	Anas platyrhinchos	+	-
Pycnonotus xanthopygos	+	-	Coturnix coturnix	(+?)	-	Milvus migrans	+	+
Lanius excubitor	+	+	Turdus merula	(+?)	-	Pernis apivorus	+	+
Passer domesticus	+	-	Serinus serinus	(+?)	-	Buteo buteo	+	+
Onychognathus tristrami	+	(+-)				Buteo rufinus	+	+
Pica pica	+	(†)				Aquila pomarina	+	+
Corvus monedula	+	-				Coturnix coturnix	+	-
Corvus ruficollis	+	(+-)				Melanocorypha calandra	+	-
Corvus rhipidurus	+	(+-)				Turdus merula	+	-
Corvus corone	+	-				Serinus serinus	+	-
						Coccothraustes coccothraustes	+	-
						Sturnus vulgaris	+	-
						Corvus monedula	+	-

Table 52
The status of the birds species in the region of Netiv Hagdud during the PPNA and at present.
- = Absent, + = Present, (+-) = Rare, (+?) = Exact status unknown, (†) = Extinct in the southern Levant.

SPECIES	FEEDING HABITATS	BREEDING HABITATS
Non-Passeriformes		
Fulica atra	Aquatic-Semi-aquatic	Aquatic-Semi-aquatic
Hoplopterus spinosus	Terrestrial, associated with freshwaters	Terrestrial, associated with freshwaters
Otis tarda	Terrestrial, steppes	Terrestrial, steppes
Leptoptilus crumeniformes	Terrestrial, associated with wetland	Savanna trees
Ciconia ciconia	Terrestrial, associated with wetland	Trees, high posts
Columba livia	Terrestrial	Cliffs
Streptopelia decaocto	Terrestrial	Trees
Tadorna tadorna	Aquatic-Semi-aquatic	Aquatic-Semi-aquatic
Anas querquedula	Aquatic	Aquatic
Anas platyrhinchos	Aquatic	Aquatic
Anser albifrons	Terrestrial-semi-aquatic	Terrestrial-semi-aquatic
Milvus migrans	Euryotopic	Trees
Pernis apivorus	Euryotopic	Trees
Buteo buteo	Woods, Forests	Cliffs and trees
Buteo rufinus	Cliffs and mountains	Cliffs
Aquila pomarina	Mixed habitats	Trees
Alectoris chukar	Terrestrial, Mediterranean to semi-desert	Terrestrial, Mediterranean to semi-desert
Francolinus francolinus	Terrestrial, marshes, wetland, grassland	Terrestrial, marshes, wetland, grassland
Ammoperdix hey	Terrestrial, semi-desert	Terrestrial, semi-desert
Coturnix coturnix	Terrestrial, Mediterranean	Terrestrial, Mediterranean
Athene noctua	Open country, Mediterranean to semi-desert	Holes in trees and cliffs
Passeriformes		
Galerida cristata	Open country, Mediterranean to semi-arid	Terrestrial
Melanocorypha calandra	Open country, Mediterranean	Terrestrial
Pycnonotus xanthopygos	Arboreal	Arboreal
Turdus merula	Arboreal	Arboreal
Lanius excubitor	Mediterranean to semi-desert shrubs	Mediterranean to semi-desert shrubs
Serinus serinus	Terrestrial and arboreal	Arboreal
Coccothraustes coccothraustes	Arboreal	Arboreal
Passer domesticus	Euryotopic, euryoecious, human habitations	Euryotopic, euryoecious, human habitations
Sturnus vulgaris	Terrestrial	Arboreal
Onychognathus tristrami	Terrestrial	Cliffs
Pica pica	Woodland, parkland	Woodland, parkland
Corvus monedula	Terrestrial	Cliffs, caves
Corvus ruficollis	Euryoecious	Cliffs, Trees
Corvus rhipidurus	Terrestrial	Cliffs
Corvus cornix	Euryoecious	Strictly arboreal

Table 53
Habitat partitioning of all the species of birds recorded and identified from Netiv Hagdud. The information is based on the recent avifauna and the present status of these birds in the Levant, or, if extinct, or unknown as breeders from the Levant, from Europe and Asia.

Species	Geographic Range	Regional Distribution	Isohyet	Habitat	Status
Insectivora					
Erinaceus concolor	Mostly European	Mediterranean	Min. 250	Euryoecious	Absent
Paraechinus aethiopicus	Afro-Arabo-Sindian	Negev and Lower Jordan Valley	Max. 170	Eremian	Uncommon
Hemiechinus auritus	North Africa to East Asia	Western Negev and Coastal dunes		Steppes, Semiarid	Absent
Rodentia					
Psammomys obesus	Saharo-Arabian	Negev, Lower Jordan Valley	Max. 100	Eremian	Abundant
Meriones tristrami	Eastern Mediterranean and northern Mesopotamia	Mediterranean	Min. 300	Batha	Absent
Spalax ehrenbergi	Southern Levant	Mediterranean and northern Negev	Min. 150	Batha	Absent
Mus musculus	Cosmopolitan	Commensal		Human settlements	Absent
Arvicola terrestris	Palearctic	Absent	Min. 600	Aquatic	Absent
Microtus guentheri	Levant	Mediterranean	Min. 300	Batha	Absent

Table 54
Present regional distribution, habitat partitioning, minimum-maximum isohyet, and local distribution and status of the small mammals recorded from Netiv Hagdud.

Species	Geographic Range	Regional Distribution	Isohyet	Habitat	Status
Lepus capensis	Trans-Palearctic and Africa	Trans-Levantine		Open Country	Common
Procavia capensis	Southern Levant, Ethiopian	Mountainous regions of the Levant		Rocky terrain	Uncommon
Vormela peregusna	Trans-Palearctic	Mediterranean to semiarid	Min. 150	Euryoecious	Absent
Meles meles	Palearctic of Eurasia	Mediterranean to semiarid	Min. 150	Euryoecious	Absent
Martes foina	Palearctic of Eurasia	Mediterranean	Min. 350	Rocky terrain	Absent*
Vulpes vulpes	Holarctic	Trans-Levantine		Euryoecious	Common
Canis familiaris	Cosmopolitan			Human settlements	Commensal
Canis aureus	Southern Palearctic	Mediterranean to semiarid		Euryoecious	Rare
Felis silvestris	Trans-Palearctic and Africa	Trans-Levantine		Euryoecious	Absent/Rare
Felis chaus	South and East Palearctic	Coastal Plain &Levantine Rift Valleys		Wetlands	Absent/Rare
Caracal caracal	Ethiopian, Oriental & central Asia	Arid to semiarid		Open country	Absent/Rare
Sus scrofa	Trans-Palearctic	Mediterranean to semiarid		Euryoecious	Absent/Rare
Bos primigenius †	Trans-Palearctic				Absent
Capra ibex nubiana	Southern Levant, upper Nile	Mountainous region of the Levantine deserts		Rocky terrain	Absent
Gazella gazella	Southern Levant	Mediterranean		Open country	Common
Alcelaphus buselaphus (†)	East and North Africa			Open country	Absent
Dama mesopotamica (?†)	Southern Mesopotamia	Irano-Turanian parkland		Parkland	Absent
Capreolus capreolus [(†)]	Palearctic (excluding Africa)	Mediterranean woodland		Woods & forests	Absent
Equus cf. *hemionus* [(†)]	Central Asia	Steppes		Open country	Absent

Table 55
Present regional distribution, habitat partitioning, minimum-maximum isohyet, and local distribution status of medium to large mammals recorded from the PPNA of the Lower Jordan Valley (Netiv Hagdud, Gilgal, Salibiya IX, and Jericho).
† = Extinct species, (†) = Extinct in Asia, (?†) = Probably extinct, [(†)] = Extinct in the Levant.

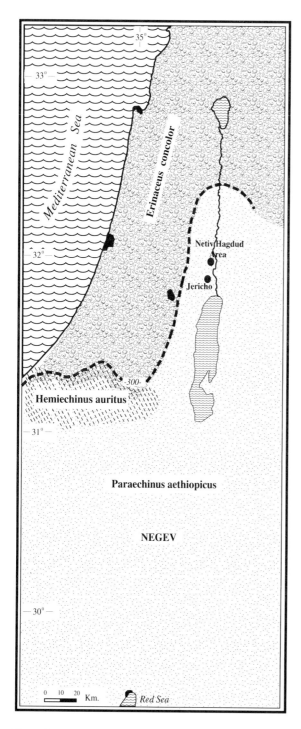

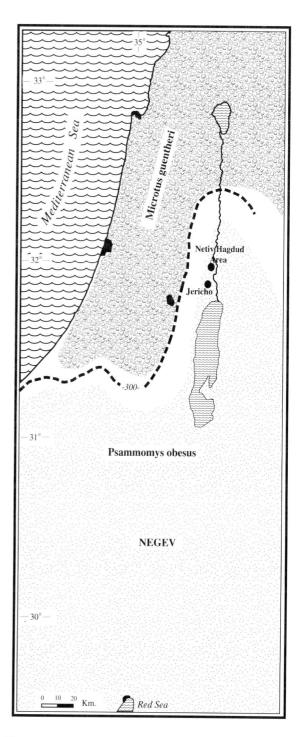

Figure 29
The present distribution of the three known species of
Erinaceidae in the southern Levant and the suggested
borderline for the 300 mm isohyet during the PPNA. All
three species are recorded at Netiv Hagdud, but only
Hemiechinus auratus exists at present in the area of Netiv
Hagdud.

Figure 30
The present distribution of *Microtus guentheri*, a typical
Mediterranean species, which is recorded at Netiv Hagdud
and the suggested borderline for the 300 mm isohyet during
the PPNA.

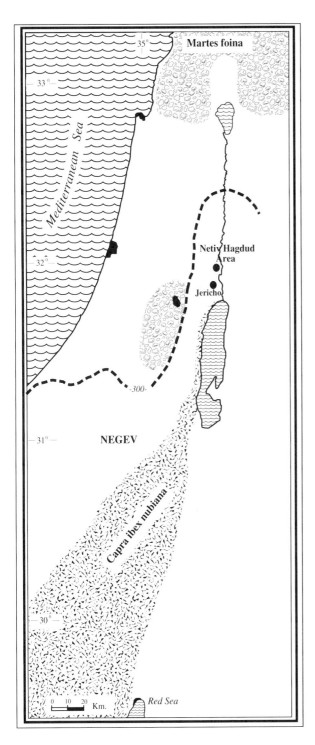

Figure 31
The present distribution of *Martes foina*, a typical
Mediterranean species, which is recorded at Netiv Hagdud
and the suggested borderline for the 300 mm isohyet during
the PPNA and the current distribution of *Capra ibex nubiana*.

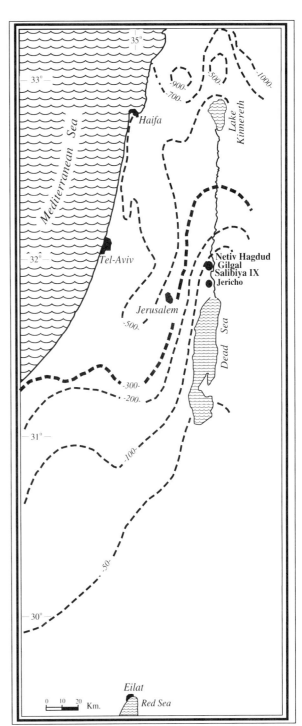

Figure 32
A multiannual isohyet map of Israel. The Lower Jordan
Valley stays at present around 100 (±25) mm, while the 300
mm line demarcates the ecological borderline between the
semi-arid region and the Mediterranean one.

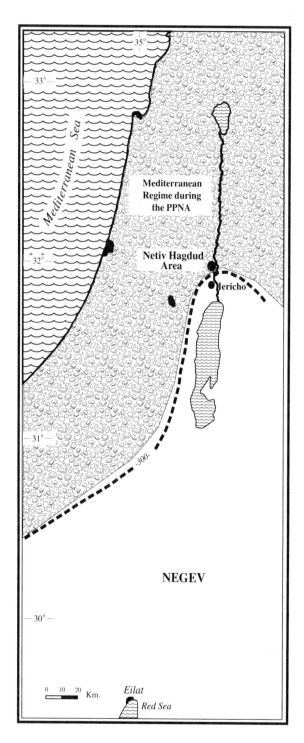

Figure 33
The present Mediterranean (±300 mm isohyet) border in the southern Levant.

decrease in steppic species in the Lower Jordan Valley. The palynological spectrum thus is in full agreement with the faunal record. A few types of trees were mentioned by Kislev (Bar-Yosef et al. 1991; Kislev et al. 1986; Kislev and Bar-Yosef 1988) which may support some of the Mediterranean faunal elements recorded from the region: *Amygdalus* sp., *Pistacia* sp., *Quercus* sp. (*calliprinos*), and *Ficus carica*. To these forms we may add *Ceratonia siliqua*, *Fontanesia*, and *Tamarix* spp. according to the pollen record (Leroi-Gourhan and Darmon 1987; Darmon 1988; Darmon et al. 1989).

On the whole it seems that the regime of higher annual precipitation contributed considerably to the success of the early farming communities. Proximity to permanent water sources was crucial for a large sedentary community. Sites located in the Jordan Rift Valley and the coastal plains are situated near water bodies many of which, like those of Netiv Hagdud and Gilgal, have long since disappeared. Tell Aswad in the Damascus Plain was located on a lake shore, and Mureybet was situated on the bank of the Euphrates River; Nemrik 9 and Qermez Dere were in somewhat similar situations. None of these sites was ever as far from open woodland when occupied as it is at present. Proximity to water bodies assured the supplies of firewood and building materials for people. Each of the early Neolithic settlements in which at least some cultivation was practiced was located on or near alluvial soils. This situation enabled the inhabitants to till land often renewed by the deposition of sediments which accumulated seasonally during the wet periods.

Other evidence for the paleoenvironmental conditions that prevailed during the PPNA in this region comes from the salty lake Lisan which covered the entire Jordan Valley during the last Glacial. It has been shown by Begin et al. (1985) and Magaritz and Goodfriend (1988) that during the arid spell of the eleventh millennium B.P., the Lisan Lake greatly receded, leaving behind a track of a flat muddy-marly lake bottom and a trail of small residual water bodies. Around 10,300 B.P. a return to a wetter phase, although not as wet as in former Upper Pleistocene phases, took place (Magaritz and Goodfriend 1988; O. Bar Yosef 1989). It was during this period that the trail of water bodies appeared in the area, considerably enriching the local biota (fig. 34). This trail of freshwater to semi-freshwater bodies could have been further enlarged during the wetter conditions that prevailed in the PPNA period and dispersed from the marshes of Fazael southward towards Jericho, as argued by O. Bar Yosef (1989). This phenomenon would explain the abundance of aquatic plants and animals in all the PPNA sites. The wetter phase could have lasted during the PPNA and the PPNB periods, greatly affecting the southern Levantine ecosystems. This wetter phase would also explain the existence of Palearctic and Mediterranean elements in much lower latitudes within the present Sinai Desert (Tchernov 1981, 1982; Tchernov and Bar Yosef 1982; Dayan et al. 1986).

The transition from the latest Pleistocene to the Holocene was marked by severe global climatic fluctuations that were manifest along arid-mesic boundaries mainly as changes in the amount of precipitation. The Younger Dryas event of the North Atlantic region was recognized in the Red Sea cores (Almogi-Lubin et al. 1991). The $\partial\,18^{\circ}$ record pointed to a

marked increase in the salinity of the Red Sea by three to five percent, indicating a coincidence of an arid phase in the region. In addition Magaritz and Goodfriend (1988:173) argued that following relatively wet conditions during the period between 12,000 to 11,000 B.P., "a short period of extremely dry conditions [ca. 1,000 years]" prevailed in the Levant. This claim is not consistent with the biological evidence that has accumulated from all the PPNA sites in the southern Levant. Yet Magaritz and Goodfriend (1988) agree that the evidence for this period "is meager since it represents a time of erosion and non-deposition of sediments." No radiocarbon dates for this period have been obtained from sediments in the northern Negev.

The brief dry and cold spell during the Late Natufian that is correlated to the European Younger Dryas (Goodfriend et al. 1986) is reflected in the levels of the Dead Sea and the Hula Valley pollen core (Baruch

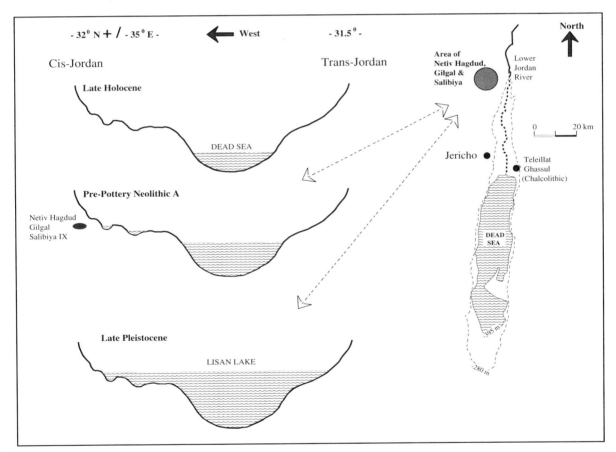

Figure 34
Transverse (east-west) sections of the status of the salty Lisan lake during the late Pleistocene (Epipaleolithic), PPNA, and early Holocene periods. A general recession of the lake is shown along the east-west geographical line of Netiv Hagdud.

and Bottema 1991). The existence of the Harifian culture in the Negev and northern Sinai, dated to 10,600 to 10,200 B.P. (Goring-Morris 1987), demonstrates human efforts to overcome climatic vagaries. The paucity of sites in this desert belt that should be dated to the ensuing PPNA period may testify to the lingering effects of the retreat of humans from this region to sowable land. A variety of paleoclimatic records points to a "major wet period in the southern Levant in the early Holocene, ca. 9,500–8,500 B.P." (Goodfriend et al. 1986:354). The Dead Sea, which shrank during the Younger Dryas, did not expand again to its former limits. Instead, a series of shallow basins within the Jordan Valley became freshwater ponds that accommodated a rich biotic environment (fig. 34).

Therefore, O. Bar-Yosef's (1989) argument that the onset of the wetter conditions around 10,300–10,000 B.P. following the eleventh millennium later Natufian drier period related to the Younger Dryas, is relevant. The event was significant enough to trigger an expansion and establishment of early Neolithic settlements, with their successful practice of hunting technology, herd culling, and cultivation in areas that are presently within the semiarid belt. The proposed reconstruction of the vegetational belts based on the palynological records (Bar-Yosef and Belfer-Cohen 1989) indicates that Netiv Hagdud was within the Mediterranean vegetational belt.

Finally, the conspicuous trend towards impoverishment of the PPNA-PPNB ecosystems during the Holocene cannot be regarded as an evolutionary process, nor a process of ecological succession. Similar to many other places in the world, the post-Pleistocene biotic turnover, usually of a catastrophic magnitude, was caused by abiotic and in some cases anthropogenic causes. The sharp and brief biotic changes that took place after the PPNA-PPNB were mainly expressed in considerable attenuation of the local communities that remained within the swiftly desiccating belt. While the evacuated niches were rapidly occupied by Eremian (mainly Arabian; Tchernov 1988) species, the total diversity greatly declined.

EPILOGUE

Anthropological and biological evidence shows that during the Natufian period human communities occupied relatively large sites on a long-term basis, in what is interpreted to be an early stage of sedentism. The shift from ephemeral and/or seasonal occupation to prolonged habitation of relatively large communities had a far reaching and profound impact on the proximate biotic environment. Due to the sedentary community's need to exploit its resources within a geographically limited area, its subsistence became ever more restricted. People were compelled to become more specialized in their use of biotic parameters. This resulted in a wide array of animal remains, including small mammals, birds, reptiles, and fishes, as well as large pulmonates. One of the most interesting phenomena that followed the long-term occupation of Natufian sites is the abrupt appearance of commensals around human habitations (Tchernov 1984, 1991a, 1991b). Cultural control of wild populations of gazelles, as expressed by the highly selective culling of males, resulted in phenotypic deformation of body proportion and size, mainly toward a drastic disproportional allometric size diminution and a highly skewed curve of the population structure (Cope 1991).

The early sedentary populations not only shifted into a broader dietary spectrum and relied on a greater proportion of smaller (lower-ranked) animal species, as argued by many archaeologists (e.g., Winterhalder 1981; Speth and Scott 1989), but the earliest villagers also continued to practice intensive and specialized hunting of large game. Yet, contrary to earlier periods, they gradually focused their hunting exclusively on a single species, which in the southern Levant was *Gazella gazella* (Legge 1972; Davis 1983; Henry 1985, 1989a; Bar-Yosef and Belfer-Cohen 1989; Tchernov 1992). As it appears unlikely that gazelles were domesticated, their high relative frequencies in the Natufian period must be the result of preferential hunting practices.

Based on gazelle-age profiles, Legge suggested that this species may have been domesticated (Legge 1972). Davis (1974) refuted this hypothesis pointing out the natural behavior of the gazelle makes it extremely unlikely that it was ever herded as a domesticate. Analysis of Natufian faunal assemblages, however, is striking for its pronounced bias toward gazelle (Legge 1972; Henry et al. 1981; Henry 1989a; Cope 1991). It is apparent that there is preference for this species in the Natufian and PPNA periods as gazelle bones consistently predominate those of other ungulates regardless of the local environment

(Henry 1975). The special attitude of the Natufian people toward gazelles may be demonstrated in three different, but interdependent aspects:

1. Gazelle remains in Natufian deposits always significantly outnumber those from all other ungulates. The exceptionally high frequency of gazelles was striking enough to engage the curiosity of many archaeozoologists who have tried to explain it in many different ways (Legge 1972; Davis 1981, 1983, 1985; Henry 1989a; Cope 1991). All of them agree that there is an apparent preferential hunting for gazelles over other large game, regardless of their local environment.

2. Intensive sex culling is another phenomenon unique to the Natufian culture. The Natufians exerted highly sophisticated, selective male culling on the local populations. The representation of males in the Natufian sites fluctuates between 60–80 percent, depending on site and date.

3. The impact of heavy hunting pressure and biased male culling affected the gazelle population to such a critical degree that part of the population underwent extensive dwarfism (Cope 1991).

Increase in the exploitation of a large variety of animal species, grains, and other plants, could only have been the consequence of overuse of an area and the draining of food resources for a long period of time. The traditional sources of animal species hunted for meat under these conditions became insufficient. Sedentary human populations were forced to rely on much less energetically rewarding (amount of meat per catch) animals (like *Lepus* and *Alectoris*), and many small species became newly and highly represented in all Natufian layers.

One of the central questions concerning these periods is whether or not a cultural continuity exists between the Natufian and the PPNA. Bar-Yosef and Belfer-Cohen (1989) argued that this issue is unjustifiably overstressed. Despite the undeniable biological persistence of the same indigenous population, both culturally and economically the PPNA marks a major autochthonous cultural change. This change is evidenced by art objects and lithic techniques, heat treatment of flint tools, uses of adzes and celts, long-distance exchange of obsidian, enlargement of the site size, and building techniques. The exploitation of vegetal sources and the possible cultivation of legumes and cereals are reflected in the types and frequencies of grinding and pounding objects. Yet, the basic concepts and technique of animal exploitation

possibly demonstrate a continuity from the Natufian tradition (Henry 1989a).

As was emphasized in the introduction, the essential importance of the PPNA period is imbedded in its comprising an intermediate or transitional phase between the Natufian period, considered the earliest large-scale substantial sedentism of human beings and localized within the Mediterranean belt of the southern Levant, and the area of the Neolithic Revolution that mainly took place within the Fertile Crescent in the northern Levant.

The emergence of the large Early Neolithic communities was already associated with either cultivated or intensively collected wild barley. Exploitation of vegetal resources seems to have greatly increased while the exploitation of animal resources continued as in the Natufian tradition, including specialized hunting of a large diversity of vertebrates, among which many small species of mammals, birds, and reptiles were represented.

The pattern of gazelle procurement changed from the end of the Natufian to the PPNA, as demonstrated in Netiv Hagdud. The reason behind this relaxation in sex and age culling of gazelles towards the end of the Natufian could have been a shift to intensive communal hunting, as argued by Campana and Crabtree (1991a, b). Their argument is based on the kill pattern found at the site of Salibiya I which produced approximately 50 percent immature gazelles, thus a close resemblance to Baharav's (1974) age profile for modern *Gazella gazella* (47 percent) (but see Edwards 1991 for an opposing opinion). The overkill structure of Salibiya I can be explained also as a catastrophic mortality due to a "communal drive" hunting strategy (Klein and Cruz-Uribe 1984). Campana's and Crabtree's (1991a,b) data for the gazelle-age profile differs from all other Natufian and PPNA sites.

The situation of incipient animal domestication in southern and central Levant during the early PPNB is unclear. In the northern Levant and in the Taurus area, however, it seems that agricultural resources were supplemented exclusively by the hunting of wild animals. In terms of the subsistence economy, then, there is little apparent distinction between the PPNA and the Early PPNB. At Ain Ghazal (Köhler-Rollefson 1989; Simmons et al. 1988; and Köhler-Rollefson et al. 1988), in the Middle PPNB, the processes of incipient animal domestication were well under way, and there is little doubt that goats were fully domesticated by the end of this phase. It is argued that domesticated cattle and sheep appeared during the Late PPNB, and pigs and dogs joined the domesticates in the final phases of the PPNB or the PPNC period, 7,500–8,000 B.P. (Köhler-Rollefson et al. 1988). The Late PPNB also witnessed an expanded exploitation of the desert-steppe regions, exemplified by sites in the eastern reaches of Syria and Jordan and in the Negev and Sinai. The patterns of arid land exploitation intensified in the final phases of the PPNB, perhaps reflecting greater emphasis on pastoralism (Bar-Yosef and Belfer-Cohen 1989; Betts 1989; Garrard et al. 1988) and/or greater interaction between hunting-and-gathering steppe dwellers with agriculturally-based villagers in more mesic areas of the Levant. However, the situation in the coastal region of northern Palestine, even as far inland as Yiftahel (Horwitz 1989), does not fit the Middle-Late-Final PPNB patterns seen elsewhere in the Levant. In this area the reliance on hunting wild game continued, with no evidence of animal husbandry at all.

The significant increase in the relative frequency of *Capra* versus *Gazella* during the transition from the PPNA to the PPNB is obvious. Yet, there is not any convincing anatomical evidence to demonstrate that these goats were already domesticated anywhere in the southern Levant during the PPNB. On the contrary, it does seem that they were, in most sites, wild. None can deny that there is an obvious shift during the PPNB, particularly along the Jordan Valley or the Levantine corridor, from extensive gazelle hunting to sometimes an exclusive reliance on goat. The reason for this phenomenal shift of acute preferences from one species to another could have been a direct consequence of an overkill of gazelles during the PPNA and the effects of prolonged sedentism.

There is also no consistent pattern for the existence of domesticated caprovids, or even incipient domestication, during the PPNB of this region as stressed by Horwitz (1989), as the only evidence for domestication is based on *Capra/Gazella* frequencies. Yet this relation is also very inconsistent in the whole region. This unclear picture is mainly due to our profound ignorance about the detailed floral and faunal composition of the PPNA and PPNB assemblages, the detailed anatomical structure of the relevant species, and the lack of common zooarchaeological methods to deal quantitatively with such problems. As a working hypothesis it may be argued that along the Levantine corridor the reliance on caprovids was more progressive than within the montane Mediterranean

belt, or the coastal plains (Yiftahel, Abu Ghosh, Nahal Oren). The large differences in the exploitation of caprovids may have been due to the critical attrition of the gazelle populations along the Jordan Valley, which compelled people to rely on the more difficult hunting of *Capra*. A complete reliance on hunting of wild (small and large) game during the PPNB is well known from sites in southern Sinai such as Wadi Tbeik and 'Ujrat el Mehed (Tchernov and Bar-Yosef 1982; Dayan et al. 1986). During this period this region was still much more mesic and allowed intensive hunting.

It does seem plausible that there is a traditional cultural and practical continuum for the exploitation of the biotic resources going all the way from early Natufian through the PPNB in the southern Levant. With only insignificant changes during the PPNA, this tradition was still employed by the PPNB populations in those areas where caprovid (whether domesticated or not) exploitation was still relatively low. When more relevant information on the zooarchaeology of these periods becomes available, both the regional socioeconomic specialization of the Neolithic populations and the evolution towards a stage of actual farming will be better understood.

Bibliography

Almogi-Lubin, A., C. Hemleben, D. Meischner, and H. Erlenkeuser
   1991   "Paleoenvironmental Events During the Last 13,000 years in the Central Red Sea as Recorded by Pteropoda." *Paleoceanography* 6:83–98.

Auffray, J. C., E. Tchernov, and E. Nevo
   1988   "Origine du commensalisme de la souris domestique (*Mus musculus domesticus*) vis-á-vis l'homme." *Comptes Rendus de l'Académie des Sciences Paris* 307:517–522.

Auffray, J. C., E. Tchernov, F. Bonhomme, G. Heth, S. Simson, and E. Nevo
   1990   "Presence and Ecological Distribution of *Mus 'spretoides'* and *Mus musculus* in Israel. Circum-Mediterranean vicariance in the genus *Mus*." *Zeitschrift für Säugetierkunde* 55: 1–10.

Baharav, D.
   1974   "Notes on the Population Structure and Biomass of the Mountain Gazelle, *Gazella gazella gazella*." *Israel Journal of Zoology* 23:39–44.
   1980   "Habitat Utilization of the Dorcas Gazelle in a Desert Saline Area." *Journal of Arid Environments* 3:161–167.
   1981   "Food Habits of the Mountain Gazelle in Semiarid Habitats of Eastern Lower Galilee, Israel." *Journal of Arid Environments* 4:63–69.
   1983a   "Observation on the Ecology of the Mountain Gazelle in the Upper Galilee, Israel." *Mammalia* 47:59–69.
   1983b   "Reproductive Strategies in Female Mountain and Dorcas Gazelles (*Gazella gazella* and *Gazella dorcas*)." *Journal of the Zoological Society of London* 200:445–453.

Bar-Yosef, D. E.
   1989   "Late Palaeolithic and Neolithic Marine Shells in Southern Levant as Cultural Markers," in *Proceedings of the 1986 Shell Bead Conference*, C. F. Hayes, ed., pp. 1169–174. Rochester Museum and Science Center, Rochester, New York.
   1991   "Changes in the Selection of Marine Shells from the Natufian to the Neolithic," in *The Natufian Culture in the Levant*, O. Bar-Yosef and F. R. Valla, eds., pp. 629–636. Archaeological

Series 1. International Monographs in Pre-history, Ann Arbor, Michigan.

Bar-Yosef, O.
1980a "A Figurine from a Khiamian Site in the Lower Jordan Valley." *Paléorient* 6: 193–200.
1980b "Prehistory of the Levant." *Annual Review of Anthropology* 9:101–131.
1983   "The Natufian of the Southern Levant," in *The Hilly Flanks and Beyond*, T. Young, P. Smith, and P. Mortenson, eds.,pp. 11–42. Studies in Ancient Oriental Civilizations 36. The Oriental Institute, Chicago.
1985   "The Stone Age of Sinai Peninsula." *La Sapienza* 38:107–122.
1986   "The Walls of Jericho." *Current Anthropology* 27:157–162.
1989   "The PPNA in the Levant—An Overview." *Paléorient* 15:57–63.

Bar-Yosef, O., and A. Belfer-Cohen
1989   "The Origins of Sedentism and Farming Communities in the Levant." *Journal of World Prehistory* 3:445–498.
1991   "From Sedentary Hunter-Gatherers to Terri-torial Farmers in the Levant," in *Between Bands and States*, S. A. Gregg, ed., pp. 181–202. Occasional Papers 9. Center for Archaeologi-cal Investigations, Southern Illinois Univer-sity, Carbondale, Illinois.
1992   "From Foraging to Farming in the Mediter-ranean Levant," in *Transitions to Agriculture in Prehistory*, A. B. Gebauer and T. D. Price, eds., pp. 21–48. Prehistory Press, Madison, Wisconsin.

Bar-Yosef, O., and A. Gopher
1994   *An Early Neolithic Village in the Jordan Valley. Part I: The Archaeology of Netiv Hagdud*. Ameri-can School of Prehistoric Research, Bulletin 43. Peabody Museum, Harvard University, Cambridge.

Bar-Yosef, O., and M. E. Kislev
1989   "Early Farming Communities in the Jordan Valley, " in *Foraging and Farming: The Evolution of Plant Exploitation*, D. R. Harris and G. C. Hillman, eds., pp. 632–642, Unwin Hyman, London.

Bar-Yosef, O., and E. Tchernov
1966   "Archaeological Finds and the Fossil Faunas of the Natufian and Microlithic Industries of Hayonim Cave." *Israel Journal of Zoology* 15:104–140.

Bar-Yosef, O., and F. R. Valla, eds.
1991   *The Natufian Culture in the Levant*. Archaeo-logical Series 1. International Monographs in Prehistory, Ann Arbor, Michigan.

Bar-Yosef, O., A. Gopher, and A. N. Goring-Morris
1980   "Netiv Hagdud: A 'Sultanian' Mound in the Lower Jordan Valley." *Paléorient* 6:201–206.

Bar-Yosef, O., A. Gopher, E. Tchernov, and M. E. Kislev
1991   "Netiv Hagdud: An Early Neolithic Village Site in the Jordan Valley." *Journal of Field Archaeology* 18:405–424.

Baruch, U., and S. Bottema
1991   "Palynological Evidence for Climatic Changes in the Levant ca. 17,000–19,000 B.P.," in *The Natufian Culture in the Levant*, O. Bar-Yosef and F. R. Valla, eds., pp. 11–20. Archaeological Series 1. International Mono-graphs in Prehistory, Ann Arbor, Michigan.

Begin, Z. B., W. Broeker, B. Buchbinder, Y. Druckman, A. Kaufman, M. Magaritz, and D. Neev
1985   "Dead Sea and Lake Lisan levels during the last 30,000 years." *Reports of the Geological Sur-vey of Israel* 29:1–17.

Bender, B.
1981   "Gatherer-hunter intensification," in *Eco-nomic Archaeology Towards an Integration of Eco-logical and Social Approaches*, A. Sheridan and G. Bailey, eds., British Archaeological Reports, International Series 96. Oxford.

Bennett, C. M.
1980   "Soundings at Dhra." *Levant* 12:30–39.

Betts, A.
1989   "The Pre-Pottery Neolithic Period in Eastern Jordan." *Paléorient* 15:147–153.

Bijlisma, R.
1982 "The Migration of Raptors Near Suez, Egypt, Autumn 1981." *Sandgrouse* 5:19–44.

Bouchud, J.
1987 *La Faune du Gisement Natufien de Mallaha (Eynan) Israël.* Memoires et Travaux du Centre de Recherche Français de Jerusalem 4. Association Paléorient, Paris.

Braidwood, R. J.
1975 *Prehistoric Men.* Scott, Foresman, Glenview, Illinois.

Braidwood, L., and R. Braidwood
1986 "Prelude to the Appearance of Village-Farming Communities in Southwestern Asia," in *Ancient Anatolia: Aspects of Change and Cultural Development (Essays in Honor of Machteld J. Mellink)*, J. V. Canby, E. Porada, B. S. Ridgeway, and T. Stech, eds., pp. 3–11. University of Wisconsin Press, Madison, Wisconsin.

Braidwood, R., and L. Braidwood
1953 "The Earliest Village Communities of Southwest Asia." *Journal of World Prehistory* 1(2):278–310

Braidwood, R., and B. Howe, eds.
1960 *Prehistoric Investigations in Iraqi Kurdistan.* Studies in Ancient Oriental Civilization 31. Oriental Institute, Chicago.

Byrd, B. F.
1992 "The Dispersal of Food Production in the Eastern Sahara, " in *Transitions to Agriculture in Prehistory*, A. B. Gebauer and T. D. Price, eds., pp. 49–62. Monographs in World Archaeology 4. Prehistory Press, Madison, Wisconsin.

Campana, D. V., and P. J. Crabtree
1991a "Communal Hunting in the Natufian of the Southern Levant: the Social and Economic Implications." *Journal of Mediterranean Archaeology* 3:223–243.
1991b "More on Communal Hunting." *Journal of Mediterranean Archaeology* 4:125–128.

Cauvin, J. C.
1977 "Les fouilles de Mureybet (1972–1974) et leur signification pour les origines de sédentarisation au Proche-Orient." *Annual of the American School of Oriental Research* 44:19–48.
1978 *Les premièrs villages de Syrie-Palestine de IXème au VIIème millénaire avant J. C.* Maison de l'Orient, Lyon.
1981 "Le problème de l'eau au Proche Orient: de l'homme prédateur aux premières sociétés hydrauliques," in *L'Homme et L'Eau en Méditerranée et au Proche Orient*, J. Metral and P. Sanlaville, eds., pp. 23–30. Presses Universitaires de Lyon, Lyon.
1987 "Chronologie relative et chronologie absolue dans le néolithique du Levant nord et d'Anatolie entre 10,000–8,000 B.P.," in *Chronologies in the Near East: Relative Chronologies and Absolute Chronology 16,000–4,000 B.P.*, O. Aurenche, F. Hours, and J. Evin, eds., pp. 325–342. British Archaeological Reports, International Series 379. Oxford.
1989 "La néolithisation au Levant et sa première diffusion," in *Néolithisation*, O. Aurenche and J. Cauvin, eds., pp. 3-36. British Archaeological Reports, International Series 516. Oxford.
1994 *Naissance des divinités, naissance de l'agriculture.* CNRS, Paris.

Chetboun, R., and E. Tchernov
1983 "Temporal and Spatial Morphological Variation in *Meriones tristrami* (Rodentia, Gerbillidae) from Israel." *Israel Journal of Zoology* 32:63–90.

Christensen, S., O. Lou, M. Miller, and H. Wohlmath
1981 "The Spring Migration of Raptors in Southern Israel and Sinai." *Sandgrouse* 3:1–42.

Clutton-Brock, J.
1971 "The Primary Food Animals of the Jericho Tell From the Proto-Neolithic to the Byzantine Period." *Levant* 3:41–55.
1978 "Early Domestication and the Ungulate Fauna of the Levant During the Pre-Pottery Neolithic Period, " in *The Environmental History of the Near and Middle East since the Ice Age*, W. C. Brice, ed., pp. 29-40. Academic Press, New York.
1979 "The Mammalian Remains From the Jericho

Tell." *Proceedings of the Prehistoric Society*
45:135–157.
1981 *Domesticated Animals from Early Times.*
University of Texas Press, Austin, Texas.

Cohen, M. N.
1977 "Population Pressure and the Origins of
Agriculture: An Archaeological Example
from the Coast of Peru," in *Origins of Agriculture*, C. A. Reed, ed., pp. 135–178. Mouton
Publishers, The Hague.

Contenson, H. de
1983 "Early Agriculture in Western Asia, in *The
Hilly Flanks and Beyond*, T. Young, P. Smith,
and P. Mortenson, eds., pp. 57–65. Studies in
Ancient Oriental Civilizations 36. University
of Chicago Press, Chicago.

Cope, C.
1991 "Gazelle Hunting Strategies in the Southern
Levant,"in *The Natufian Culture in the Levant*,
O. Bar-Yosef and F. R. Valla, eds., pp. 341–358.
Archaeological   Series 1. International
Monographs in Prehistory, Ann Arbor,
Michigan.

Cramp, S., and K. E. L. Simmons
1980 *Handbook of the Birds of Europe, the Middle East
and North Africa*. Volume II. Oxford University Press, Oxford.

Crowfoot-Payne, J.
1983 "The Flint Industries of Jericho," in *Excavations at Jericho*, vol. V, K. A. Kenyon and T. A.
Holland, eds. British School of Archaeology
in Jerusalem, London.

Danin, A.
1988 "Flora and Vegetation of Israel and Adjacent
Areas," in *The Zoogeography of Israel*, Y. Yom-
Tov and E. Tchernov, eds., pp. 129–157. Dr.
W. Junk Publishers, The Hague.

Darmon, F.
1988 "Essai de reconstitution climatique de l'Épi-
paléolithique au début du Néolithique
ancien dans la région de Fazaël-Salibiya
(basse vallée du Jourdain) d'après la paly-

nologie." *Comptes Rendus de l'Académie des Sciences Paris* 307:677–682.

Darmon, F., A. Emery-Barbier, and A. Leroi-Gourhan
1989 "Exemples d'occupation régionale au
Proche-Orient en fonction des variations
paléoclimatiques." *Cahiers du Quaternaire*
13:21–38.

Davis, S.
1974 "Animal Remains from the Kebaran Site of
Ein-Gev I: Jordan Valley, Israel." *Paléorient*
2:453–462.
1981 "The Effect of Temperature Change and
Domestication on the Body Size of Late Pleistocene to Holocene Mammals." *Paleobiology*
7:101–114.
1983 "The Age Profiles of Gazelles Predated by
Ancient Man in Israel: Possible Evidence for
a Shift from Seasonality to Sedentism in the
Natufian." *Paléorient* 9:55–62.
1985 "A Preliminary Report of the Fauna of
Hatoula: A Natufian-Khiamian (PPNA) site
near Latroun, Israel," in *Le Site Natoufien-Khiamien de Hatoula près de Latroun, Israël*, M.
Lechevallier and A. Ronen, eds., pp. 71–118.
Cahiers du Centre de Recherche Français de
Jerusalem, no. 1.
1991 "When and Why Did Prehistoric People
Domesticate Animals," in *The Natufian Cul-
ture in the Levant*, O. Bar-Yosef and F. R. Valla,
eds., pp. 381–390. Archaeological Series 1.
International Monographs in Prehistory,
Ann Arbor, Michigan.

Davis, S., and F. Valla.
1978 "Evidence for Domestication of the Dog
12,000 Years Ago in the Natufian of Israel."
Nature 276:608–610.

Dayan, T., E. Tchernov, O. Bar-Yosef, and Y. Yom-Tov
1986 "Animal Exploitation in Ujrat-el-Mehed, a
Neolithic Site in Southern Sinai." *Paléorient*
12:105–116.

Dayan, T., E. Tchernov, Y. Yom-Tov, and D. Simberloff
1989 "Ecological Character Displacement in
Saharo-Arabian *Vulpes*: Outfoxing
Bergmann's Rule." *Oikos* 55:263–272.

Dor, M.
1947 "Observation sur les micromammifères trouvés dans les pelotes de la chouette effraye (*Tyto alba*) en Palestine." *Mammalia* 10:50–54.

Ducos, P.
1968 *L'origine des animaux domestiques en Palestine*. Publication de l'Institut de Préhistoire de l'Université de Bordeaux 6. Delmas, Bordeaux.
1978 "'Domestication' Defined and Methodological Approaches to its Recognition," in *Approaches to Faunal Analysis in the Middle East*, R. H. Meadow and M. Zeder, eds., pp. 53–56. Peabody Museum Bulletin, vol. 2. Peabody Museum of Archaeology and Ethnology, Harvard University, Cambridge.

Echegaray, J. G.
1966 *Excavation en la Terraza de El-Khiam (Jordania), Part II. Los Niveles Meso-Neolíticos, Estrudio de la Fauna, Flora y Análisis de las Tierras del Yacimento*. Casa Española en Jerusalem, Madrid.

Echegeray, J. G., and L. G. Freeman
1989 "A Reevaluation of El Khiam (Desert of Judea)." *Aula Orientalis* 7:37–66.

Edwards, P. C.
1989 "Problems of Recognizing the Earliest Sedentism: The Natufian Example." *Journal of Mediterranean Archaeology* 2:5–48.
1991 "More Than One, Less Than Five Hundred: Comments on Campana and Crabtree, and Communal Hunting." *Journal of Mediterranean Archaeology* 4:109–120.

Garfinkel, Y.
1990 "Gesher, un nouveau site Néolithique Précéramique A dans la moyenne valée du Jourdain, Israël." *L'Anthropologie* 94:903–906.

Garfinkel, Y., and D. Nadel
1989 "The Sultanian Flint Assemblage from Gesher and its Implications for Recognizing Early Neolithic Entities in the Levant." *Paléorient* 15:139–152.

Garner, H. F.
1975 "Rain Forests, Deserts and Evolution." *Annual Academy, Brasil, Ciencias* 47 (suppl.):127–133.

Garrard, A. N., A. Betts, B. Byrd, and C. Hunt
1988 "Prehistoric Environments and Settlement in the Azraq Basin: an Interim Report on the 1984 Season." *Levant* 18:1–20.

Goodfriend, G. A., M. Magaritz, and I. Carmi
1986 "A High Stand of the Dead Sea at the End of the Neolithic Period: Paleoclimatic and Archaeological Implications." *Climatic Change* 9:349–356.

Goring-Morris, A. N.
1987 *At the Edge: Terminal Pleistocene Hunter-Gatherers in the Negev and Sinai*. British Archaeological Reports, International Series 361. Oxford.

Grayson, D. K.
1984 *Quantitative Zooarchaeology*. Academic Press, New York.

Harrison, D. L.
1968 *Mammals of Arabia. Volume II*. Ernest Benn Ltd., London.
1972 *The Mammals of Arabia. Volume III: Lagomorpha and Rodentia*. Ernest Benn Ltd., London.

Harrison, D. L., and P. J. J. Bates
1991 *The Mammals of Arabia*. 2nd ed. Harrison Zoological Museum, Sevenoaks, England.

Hassan, F. A.
1977 "The Dynamics of Agricultural Origins in Palestine: A Theoretical Model," in *Origins of Agriculture*, C. A. Reed, ed., pp. 589–610. Mouton Publishers, The Hague.
1981 *Demographic Archaeology*. Academic Press, New York.

Hayden, B.
1990 "Nimrods, Piscators, Pluckers, and Planters: the emergence of food production." *Journal of Anthropological Archaeology* 9:31–69.

Hecker, H. M.

1975   "The Faunal Analysis of the Primary Food
        Animals from Pre-Pottery Neolithic Beidha
        (Jordan)." Ph.D. Thesis, Columbia Univer-
        sity. University Microfilms, Ann Arbor,
        Michigan.

Henry, D. O.

1975   "Fauna in Near Eastern Archeological
        Deposits," in *Problems in Prehistory: North
        Africa and the Levant*, F. Wendorf, ed., pp. 379–
        385. Southern Methodist University, Dallas.

1983   "Adaptive Evolution Within the Epipaleolith-
        ic of the Near East," in *Advances in World
        Archaeology*, vol. 2, F. Wendorf and A. E.
        Close, eds., pp. 99–160. Academic Press,
        New York.

1985   "Preagriculture Sedentism: The Natufian
        Example." in *Prehistoric Hunter-Gatherers: the
        Emergence of Complex Societies*, T. D. Price and J.
        A. Brown, eds., pp. 365–384. Academic
        Press, New York.

1989a   *Epipaleolithic of the Near East*. University of
        Pennsylvania Press, Philadelphia.

1989b   *From Foraging to Agriculture: The Levant at the
        End of the Ice Age*. University of Pennsylvania
        Press, Philadelphia.

Henry, D. O., A. Leroi-Gourhan, and S. Davis

1981   "The Excavation of Hayonim Terrace: An
        Examination of Terminal Pleistocene Climat-
        ic and Adaptive Changes." *Journal of Archaeo-
        logical Science* 8:33–58.

Hesse, B.

1975   "Rodent Remains and Sedentism in the
        Neolithic: Evidence from Tepe Ganj Dareh,
        Western Iran." *Journal of Mammalogy* 60:856–
        857.

1984   "These Are Our Goats: The Origins of Herd-
        ing in West Central Iran," in *Animals and
        Archaeology: 3. Early Herders and their Flocks*, J.
        Clutton-Brock and C. Geigso, eds., pp. 243–
        264. British Archaeological Reports, Interna-
        tional Series 202. Oxford.

Hillman, G. C., S. M. Colledge, and D. R. Harris.

1989   "Plant-Food Economy During the Epipale-
        olithic Period at Tell Abu Hureyra, Syria:
        Dietary Diversity, Seasonality, and Modes of
        Exploitation," in *Foraging and Farming: the
        Evolution of Plant Exploitation*, D. R. Harris and
        G. C. Hillman, eds., pp. 240–268. Unwin
        Hyman, London.

Horwitz, L. K.

1989   "A Reassessment of Caprovine Domestication
        in the Levantine Neolithic: Old Question,
        New Answer," in *People and Culture in Change*,
        I. Hershkowitz, ed., pp. 53–181. British
        Archaeological Reports, International Series
        508(i). Oxford.

Horwitz, K. L., and Y. Garfinkel

1992   "Animal Remains From the Site of Gesher,
        Central Jordan Valley." *Mitekufat Haeven, Jour-
        nal of the Israel Prehistory Society* 24:64–76.

Horwitz, L. K., C. Cope, and E. Tchernov

1991   "Sexing the Bones of Mountain Gazelle
        (*Gazella gazella*) From Prehistoric Sites in the
        Southern Levant." *Paléorient* 16:1–11.

Hovers, E.

1989   "Settlement and Subsistence Patterns in the
        Lower Jordan Valley from Epipalaeolithic to
        Neolithic Times," in *People and Culture in
        Change*, I. Hershkowitz, ed., pp. 37–52.
        British Archaeological Reports, International
        Series 508(i). Oxford.

Hovers, E., L. K. Horwitz, D. E. Bar-Yosef, and
C. Cope-Miyashiro

1988   "The Site of Urkan-E-Rub IIa: A Case Study
        of Subsistence and Mobility Patterns in the
        Kebaran Period in the Lower Jordan Valley."
        *Mitekufat Haeven, Journal of the Israel Prehistory
        Society* 21:20–48.

Jacobs, L. L., and D. Pilbeam

1980   "Of Mice and Men: Fossil-Based Divergence
        Dates and Molecular 'Clocks'." *Journal of
        Human Evolution* 9:551–555.

Kenyon, K. M.

1957   *Digging Up Jericho*. Ernest Benn, London.

1981   *Excavations at Jericho. Vol. III. The Architecture
        and Stratigraphy of the Tell*. British School of
        Archaeology in Jerusalem, London.

Kenyon, K. M., and T. A. Holland
1983 *Excavations at Jericho. Vol. V. The Pottery Phases of the Tell and Other Finds.* British School of Archaeology in Jerusalem, London.

Kislev, M. E., and O. Bar-Yosef
1988 "The Legumes: The Earliest Domesticated Plants in the Near East?" *Current Anthropology* 29:175–179.

Kislev, M. E., O. Bar-Yosef, and A. Gopher
1986 "Early Neolithic Domesticated and Wild Cereals from Netiv Hagdud Region in the Jordan Valley." *Israel Journal of Botany* 35:197–201.

Klein, R. G., and K. Cruz-Uribe
1984 *The Analysis of Animal Bones from Archaeological Sites.* University of Chicago Press, Chicago.

Köhler-Rollefson, L.
1989 "Changes in Goat Exploitation at 'Ain Ghazal Between the Early and Late Neolithic: A Metrical Analysis. *Paléorient* 15:141–146.

Köhler-Rollefson, L., W. Gillespie, and M. Metzger
1988 "The Fauna from Neolithic 'Ain Ghazal," in *The Prehistory of Jordan. The State of Research in 1986*, vol. 2, D. A. Garrard and H. Gebel, eds., pp. 423–430. British Archaeological Reports, International Series 396(ii). Oxford.

Kuijt, I., J. Mabry, and G. Palumbo
1991 "Early Neolithic Use of Upland Areas of Wadi el-Yabis: Preliminary Evidence From the Excavations of 'Iraq ed-Dubb, Jordan." *Paléorient* 17: 99–108.

Lechevallier, M., and A. Ronen
1985 *Le site Natoufien-Khiamien de Hatoula près de Latroun, Israel.* Cahiers du Centre de Recherche Français de Jerusalem, no. 1.
1989 "L'occupation post-Natoufienne de Hatoula, en Judée occidentale, et sa place dans le carde regional," in *Investigations in South Levantine Prehistory*, O. Bar-Yosef and B. Vandermeersch, eds., pp. 309–321. British Archaeological Reports, International Series 497. Oxford.

Lechevallier, M., D. Philibert, A. Ronen, and A. Samzun
1989 "Une occupation Khiamienne et Sultanienne à Hatoula (Israël)?" *Paléorient* 15:1-10.

Legge, T.
1972 "Prehistoric Exploration of the Gazelle in Palestine," in *Papers in Economic Prehistory*, E. S. Higgs, ed., pp. 119–124. Cambridge University Press, Cambridge.

Leroi-Gourhan, A., and F. Darmon
1987 Analyses palynologiques de sites archéologiques du Pleistocène final dans la vallée du Jourdain. *Journal of Earth Sciences* 36:65–72.

Lieberman, D. E.
1993 "Mobility and Strain: The Biology of Cementogenesis and its Application to the Evolution of Hunter-Gatherer Seasonal Mobility during the Late Quaternary in the Southern Levant." Ph.D. Thesis, Department of Anthropology, Harvard University, Cambridge, Massachusetts.

Magaritz, M., and G. A. Goodfriend
1988 "Movement of the Desert Boundary in the Levant from Latest Pleistocene to Early Holocene," in *Abrupt Climatic Change*, W. H. Berger and L. D. Labeyrie, eds, pp. 173–183. D. Reidel Publishing Company, Boston.

Mellaart, J.
1975 *The Neolithic of the Near East.* Thames and Hudson, London.

Mendelssohn, H., and H. Steinitz
1944 "Contributions to the Ecological Zoogeography of the Amphibians in Palestine." *Review of the Faculty of Science, University of Istanbul, Series B* 9:289–298.

Mienis, H.
1983 "A Preliminary Checklist of the Freshwater Molluscs of Israel and the Administered Areas." *Levantina* 47:543–550.

Moore, A. M. T.
1983   "The First Farmers in the Levant," in *The Hilly Flanks and Beyond*, T. C. Young, P. E. L. Smith and P. Mortensen, eds., pp. 91–111. Studies In Ancient Oriental Civilizations 36. University of Chicago Press, Chicago.
1985   "The Development of Neolithic Societies in the Near East," in *Advances in World Archaeology*, vol. 4, F. Wendorf and A. Close, eds., pp. 1–69. Academic Press, New York.
1989   "The Transition from Foraging to Farming in Southwest Asia," in *Foraging and Farming: The Evolution of Plant Exploitation*, D. R. Harris and G. C. Hilman, eds., pp. 620–631. Unwin Hyman, London.

Moore, A. M. T., and G. C. Hillman
1992   "The Pleistocene to Holocene Transition and Human Economy in Southwest Asia: The Impact of the Younger Dryas." *American Antiquity* 57:482–494.

Neuville, R.
1951   *Le Paléolithique et le Mésolithique du Désert de Judée*. Mémoire 24. Archives de l'Institute Paléontologique Humaine, Paris.

Nevo, E., E. Tchernov, and A. Beiles
1988   "Morphometrics of Speciating Mole Rats: Adaptive Differences in Ecological Speciation." *Zeitschrift für Zoologische Systematik und Evolutionforschung* 26:286–314.

Noe-Nygaard, N.
1987   "Taphonomy in archaeology." *Journal of Danish Archaeology* 6:7–62.

Noy, T.
1989   "Gilgal 1. A Pre-Pottery Neolithic Site in Northern Iraq." *Paléorient* 15:11–18.

Noy, T., J. Legge, and E. S. Higgs
1973   "Recent Excavations at Nahal Oren." *Proceedings of the Prehistoric Society* 39:75–99.

Noy, T., J. Schuldenrein, and E. Tchernov
1980   "Gilgal, a Pre-Pottery Neolithic A Site on the Lower Jordan Valley." *Israel Exploration Journal* 30:63–82.

Orsini, P., F. Bonhomme, J. Britton-Davidian, H. Croset, S. Gerasimov, and L. Thaler
1983   "Le complex d'espèces du genre *Mus* en Europe Centrale et Orientale. II-critères d'identification, répartitions et caractéristiques écologiques." *Zeitschrift für Säugetierkunde* 48:86–95.

Osborn, D. J., and I. Helmy
1980   *The Contemporary Land Mammals of Egypt Including Sinai*. Fieldiana Zoology, New Series 5:1–579.

Pichon, J.
1984   "L'Avifaune Natufiennne du Levant. Systématique, Paléoecologie, Paléoethnozoologie." These 3è Cycle. Université Pierre et Marie Curie No. 84–58. Unpublished Dissertation.
1987   "L'Avifaune dans l'ouvrage collectif: 'La faune du vilage de Mallaha (Eynan), Israël'," in *La Faune du Gisement Natufien de Mallaha (Eynan) Israel*, J. Bouchud, ed., pp. 115–150. Memoires et Travaux du Centre de Recherche Français de Jerusalem 4. Association Paléorient, Paris.
1989   "L'environement du Natufien en Israël," in *Investigations in South Levantine Prehistory*, O. Bar-Yosef and B. Vandermeersch, eds., pp. 61–74. British Archaeological Reports, International Series 497. Oxford.

Ranck, G. L.
1968   "The Rodents of Libya." *Taxonomy, Ecology and Zoogeographical Relationships*. Smithsonian Institution Bulletin 275:1–264. U.S. National Museum, Washington, D.C. .

Redding, W. R.
1988   "A General Explanation of Subsistence Change: from Hunting and Gathering to Food Production." *Journal of Anthropological Archaeology* 7:56–97.

Redman, C.
1978   *The Rise of Civilization*. Freeman, San Francisco.

Ronen, A., and M. Lechevallier
1985   "The Natufian-Early Neolithic Site Hamla, Near Latrun, Israel." *Quartär* 35/36:141–164.

1991   "The Natufian of Hatoula," in *The Natufian Culture in the Levant*, O. Bar-Yosef and F. R. Valla, eds., pp. 149–160. Archaeological Series 1. International Monographs in Prehistory, Ann Arbor, Michigan.

Rull, V.
1990   "Quaternary Palaeoecology and Ecological Theory." *Orsis* 5:91–111.

Schuldenrein, J., and P. Goldberg
1982   "Late Quaternary Palaeoenvironments and Prehistoric Sites in the Lower Jordan Valley: a Preliminary Report." *Paléorient* 7:57–71.

Schütt, H.
1983   "Die Molluskenfauna der Subwasser im Einzugsgebiet des Orontes unter Berucksichtigung benachbarter Flubsysteme." *Archiv für Molluskenkunde* 113:17–91.

Schwartz, E., and H. K. Schwartz
1943   "The Wild and Commensal Stocks of the House Mouse, *Mus musculus* Linnaeus." *Journal of Mammalogy* 24:59–72.

Setzer, H. W.
1957   "A Review of the Libyan Mammals." *Journal of the Egyptian Public Health Association* 21:41–82.

Simmons, A.H., I. Köhler-Rollefson, G. O. Rollefson, R. Mandel, and Z. Kafari
1988   " 'Ain-Ghazal: A Major Neolithic Settlement in Central Jordan." *Science* 240:35–39.

Sinclair, A. R. F.
1974   "The Natural Regulation of Buffalo Populations in East Africa. IV: The Food Supply as a Regulating Factor and Competition." *East African Wildlife Journal* 12:129–311.
1975   "The Resource Limitation of Trophic Levels in Tropical Grassland Ecosystems." *Journal of Animal Ecology* 44:497–520.

Smith, P.
1972   "Diet and Attrition in the Natufians." *American Journal of Physical Anthropology* 37:233–238.

Solecki, S., and T. H. McGovern
1980   "Predatory Birds and Prehistoric Man," in *Theory and Practice: Essays presented to Gene Weltfish*, S. Diamond, ed., pp. 79–95. Mouton Publishers, The Hague.

Solecki, R. S., and R. L. Solecki
1983   "Late Pleistocene-Early Holocene Cultural Tradition in the Zagros, " in *The Hilly Flanks and Beyond*, C. T. Young, Ph. E. L. Smith, and P. Mortensen, eds., pp. 123–137. Studies in Ancient Oriental Civilization 36. Oriental Institute, University of Chicago Press, Chicago.

Speth, J. D.
1983   *Bison Kills and Bone Counts: Decision Making by Ancient Hunters.* University of Chicago Press, Chicago.
1987   "Early Hominid Subsistence Strategies in Seasonal Habitats." *Journal of Archaeological Science*, 14:1329.
1989   "Early Hominid Hunting and Scavenging: The Role of Meat as an Energy Source." *Journal of Human Evolution* 18:329–343.

Speth, J. D., and S. L. Scott
1989   "Horticulture and Large-Mammal Hunting: the Role of Resource Depletion and the Constraints of Time and Labor, " in *Farmers and Hunters*, S. Kent, ed., pp. 71–79. Cambridge University Press, Cambridge.

Speth, J. D., and K. Spielmann
1983   "Energy Source, Protein Metabolism and Hunter-Gatherer Subsistence Strategies." *Journal of Anthropological Archaeology* 2:1–31.

Stekelis, M., and T. Yizraeli
1963   "Excavations at Nahal Oren (Preliminary Report)." *Israel Exploration Journal* 13:1–12.

Tchernov, E.
1962   "Paleolithic Avifauna in Palestine." *Bulletin of the Research Council of Israel* 11:95–131.
1968   *Succession of Rodent Faunas during the Upper Pleistocene of Israel.* Mammalia Depicta, Paul Parey, Hamburg and Berlin.

1973 *On the Pleistocene Molluscs of the Jordan Valley*. The Israel Academy of Sciences and Humanities, Jerusalem.

1975a "Rodent Faunas and Environmental Changes in the Pleistocene of Israel," in *Rodents in Desert Environments*, I. Prakash and D. K. Ghosh, eds., pp. 331–362. Dr. W. Junk Publishers, The Hague.

1975b *The Early Pleistocene Molluscs of 'Erq-el-Ahmar*. The Israel Academy of Sciences and Humanities, Jerusalem, pp. 1–36.

1980 *The Pleistocene Birds of 'Ubeidiya, Jordan Valley*. The Israel Academy of Sciences and Humanities, Jerusalem, pp. 1–83.

1981 "The Impact of the post-Glacial on the Fauna of Southwest Asia, " in *Contributions to the Environmental History of Southwest Asia*, W. Frey and H. P. Uerpmann, eds., pp. 197–216. Beihefte Zum Tübinger Atlas Des Vorderen Orients, Reihe A, Naturwissenschaften 8. Weisbaden.

1982 "Faunal Responses to Environmental Changes in the Middle East During the Last 20,000 years, " in *Palaeoclimates, Palaeoenvironments, and Human Commmunities in the Eastern Mediterranean Region in Later Prehistory*, J. L. Bintliff and W. van Zeist, eds., pp. 105–127. British Archaeological Reports, International Series 133. Oxford.

1984 "Commensal Animals and Human Sedentism in the Middle East, " in *Animals and Archaeology: 3. Early Herders and their Flocks*, J. Clutton-Brock and C. Grigson, eds., pp. 91–115. British Archaeological Reports, International Series 202. Oxford.

1986 *The Lower Pleistocene Mammals of 'Ubeidiya (Jordan Valley)*. Memoires et Travaux du Centre de Recherches Prehistoriques Français de Jerusalem, No. 5, pp. 1–405. Association Paléorient, Paris.

1988 "The Paleobiogeographical History of the Southern Levant, " in *The Zoogeography of Israel*, Y. Yom-Tov and E. Tchernov, eds., pp. 159–250. Dr. W. Junk Publishers, The Hague.

1991a "Of Mice and Men. Biological Markers for Long-Term Sedentism; a Reply." *Paléorient*, 17:153–160.

1991b "Biological Evidence for Human Sedentism in Southwest Asia During the Natufian," in *The Natufian Culture in the Levant*, O. Bar-Yosef and F. R. Valla, eds., pp. 315–340. Archaeological Series 1. International Monographs in Prehistory, Ann Arbor, Michigan.

1992 "Evolution of Complexities, Exploitation of the Biosphere and Zooarchaeology." *Archaeo-Zoologia* 5:9–42.

Tchernov, E., and O. Bar-Yosef
1982 "Animal Exploitation in the Pre-Pottery Neolithic B Period at Wadi Tbeik, Southern Sinai." *Paléorient* 8:17–37.

Tchernov, E., and L. K. Horwitz
1991 "Body Size Diminution Under Domestication: Unconscious Selection in Primeval Domesticates." *Journal of Anthropological Archaeology* 10:54–75.

Tchernov, E., T. Dayan, and Y. Yom-Tov
1986 "The Paleo-Geography of *Gazella gazella* and *Gazella dorcas* During the Holocene of the Southern Levant." *Israel Journal of Zoology* 34:51–59.

Valla, F.
1987 "Chronologie absolue et chronologies relatives dans le Natoufien", in *Chronologies in the Near East: Relative Chronologies and Absolute Chronology 16,000–4,000 B.P.*, pp. 267–294. British Archaeological Reports, International Series 379. Oxford.

Walker, D., and Y. Chen
1987 "Palynological Light on Tropical Rainforest Dynamics." *Quaternary Scientific Review* 6:77–92.

Werner, Y. L.
1988 "Herpetofaunal Survey of Israel (1950–85), with Comments on Sinai and Jordan and on Zoogeographical Heterogeneity," in *The Zoogeography of Israel*, Y. Yom-Tov and E. Tchernov, eds., pp. 355–388. Dr. W. Junk Publishers, The Hague.

Winterhalder, B.
1981 "Optimal Foraging Strategies and Hunter-Gatherer Research in Anthropology: Theory and Models, " in *Hunter-Gatherer Foraging Strategies*, B. Winterhalder and A. E. Smith,

eds., pp. 13–35. University of Chicago Press, Chicago.

Yom-Tov, Y.
  1988   "The Zoogeography of the Birds and Mammals of Israel," in *The Zoogeography of Israel*, Y. Yom-Tov and E. Tchernov, eds., pp. 389–410. Dr. W. Junk Publishers, The Hague.

Zeist, W. van
  1986   "Some Aspects of Early Neolithic Plant Husbandry in the Near East." *Anatolica* 15:49–67.

Zeist, W. van, and J. A. H. Bakker-Heeres
  1985   "Archaeobotanical Studies in the Levant. 1. Neolithic Sites in the Damascus Basin: Aswad, Ghoraifé, Ramad." *Palaeohistoria* 24:165–256.
  1986   "Archaeobotanical Studies in the Levant. 3. Late Paleolithic Muryebit." *Palaeohistoria* 26:!71–199.

Zohary, D.
  1989   "Domestication of the Southwest Asian Neolithic Crop Assemblage of Cereals, Pulses, and Flux: the Evidence from Living Plants, " in *Foraging and Farming*, D. R. Harris and G. C. Hillman, eds., pp. 358–373. Unwin Hyman, London.

Zohary, D., and M. Hopf
  1988   *Domestication of Plants in the Old World*. Clarendon Press, Oxford.

Zohary, M.
  1973   *Geobotanical Foundations of the Middle East*. Gustav Fischer, Stutgart.

Zuckerbrott, Y. D., U. N. Safriel, and U. Paz
  1980   "Autumn Migration of Quail (*Coturnix coturnix*) at the North Coast of the Sinai Peninsula." *Ibis* 122:1–14.